The Uses of Adversity

THE USES OF ADVERSITY

LEONARD TUSHNET

New York · Thomas Yoseloff · London

© 1966 by A. S. Barnes and Co., Inc.

Library of Congress Catalogue Card Number: 65-17210

Thomas Yoseloff, *Publisher*
South Brunswick, N. J.

Thomas Yoseloff Ltd.
18 Charing Cross Road
London W.C.2, England

6287

Printed in United States of America

To the memory of Isadore Brandchaft

Acknowledgments

For permission to reproduce the photographs and sketches used in this book, thanks are given to the Jewish Historical Institute of Warsaw, Mr. Moses Leavitt, of the American Joint Distribution Committee, and Mr. Jonas Turkow.

For many valuable suggestions and encouragement, I wish especially to thank Miss Dina Abramowicz, of the YIVO Institute for Jewish Research.

I am grateful also for technical and other help given by Miss Reesa Serwatka, Mrs. Catherine Coleman, Mrs. Tessie Podesfinski, Mr. Emil Wujciak, the Jewish Historical Institute of Warsaw, the *Centre du Documentation Juive Contemporaine* of Paris, the staff of the Maplewood (N. J.) Public Library, and Mr. Leon Summit.

And finally, to those seven doctors, the only surviving participants of the research on starvation in the Ghetto, my deep appreciation for their patience in answering my questions.

LEONARD TUSHNET

Introduction

Non omnis moriar! In these words Horace expressed the poet's dream that his work would live on after his death. In a larger sense they speak of man's hope that some part of his life will be remembered, will remain behind after he has left this world. To the physicians confined in the Warsaw Ghetto they had still another meaning—the wish that the research conducted in the shadow of death should become part of the immortal body of knowledge, a permanent memorial to the brave medical men and women who perished as a result of the pseudo-science of the Nazis.

Physicians and other scientific workers are not aware, unless they are interested in problems of nutrition and have an historical outlook, that during the years of the German occupation of Poland medical research of high calibre was being carried on by doctors proscribed by the conquerors. This lack of awareness is understandable. Who could expect anything good to come out of countries subjugated by the Third Reich? Interest in the political aspects of the period has created indifference to the scientific work done in that time and in those places. And there is yet another reason, based in human psychology. We want to forget "atrocity stories." Consequently, research that was done in unbelievable circumstances with the most meticulous detail, basic studies and clinical observation, controlled and crucial experiments, all are almost forgotten. Even doctors who do not believe it beneath their dignity to examine sputum and urines and feces turn away from the examination of the foul depths of the Nazi era. Alas! Their turning away leads them to lose sight of the fact that at the same time that there were Sauerbruchs[1] there were also spirits of lesser fame but greater humanity struggling unselfishly in the interests of science.

The tale of the work done in the Warsaw Ghetto from 1940 to 1943 should be retold so that those of us who "little note nor long remember" may take pride in the fact that the group of men—physicians—so praised by Robert Louis Stevenson and so often denigrated as mere technicians contains men and women trained to rise above man's inhumanity to man.

Contents

Illustrations

We are part of the divine power against evil—widening the skirts of light and making the struggle with darkness narrower.

—George Eliot, Middlemarch

The Uses of Adversity

1. Life in the Ghetto

THE WARSAW GHETTO HAS BEEN DESCRIBED MANY TIMES, IN official documents and private accounts as well as in fiction. John Hersey's book *The Wall* gives probably the best portrayal in English of how people lived in the Ghetto, but, being a novel, it necessarily omits some of the details necessary for a thorough understanding of the reasons why the Ghetto physicians undertook the study of starvation.

After the surrender of Warsaw to the Germans on September 27, 1939, the Jewish community underwent a series of attacks by the invaders, calculated to break down morale, to make them recognize that they were "sub-humans," slaves of their Nazi masters. The *Kehillah* (Jewish Community Council) was dissolved on October 4, and a *Judenrat* (Jewish Council) set up to facilitate the carrying out of the German orders by the Jews and, incidentally, to take over the social and cultural functions of the *Kehillah*. In June 1940, the *Judenrat's* duties were limited by decree to the execution of the orders of the German authorities. In September 1940, a "Quarantine Area" was marked out, a section containing 240,000 Jews and 80,000

Christians. On October 16, all Christians were given two
weeks to move out of the area and all Jews resident in
other parts of Warsaw were ordered to move into it. On
November 15, 1940, the Quarantine Area—now called by
the Nazis the "Jewish Residential District"—was sealed by
the walling off of thoroughfares, windows, doors, open
spaces, etc.;[1] it consisted of nine square miles in the poorest part of Warsaw—1692 houses in all.[2] In January 1941, a
census showed 378,979 Jews in the Ghetto; in the next
four months this number was increased by the approxi-
mately 72,000 Jews deported from other regions of Poland
and, to some extent, from other occupied countries. In
May 1941, half a million Jews were registered in the
Ghetto, but the Germans stated that there were many
more "illegal" inhabitants there. On October 5, 1941, the
death penalty was established for leaving the Ghetto without permission. On October 23, the Small Ghetto was
abolished and the residents were driven into the Large
Ghetto. On December 1, 1941, all food packages from
outside relief organizations were forbidden to be received;
those sent were confiscated. The extermination program,
euphemistically called "resettlement," began on July 22,
1942. 380,000 Jews were registered at that time in the
Ghetto. By September 21, 1942, the Ghetto area had been
reduced by half and three-quarters of its population re-
moved from Warsaw to the extermination camps. In January 1943, only 40,000 Jews were left in the Ghetto. An
attempt was made to remove this remnant on January 18,
but was unsuccessful because of the resistance movement.
The Ghetto was finally liquidated on May 16, 1943, after a
month of fighting. It was bombed, set afire, and then the
buildings were razed,[3] including a chapel, a mortuary, and
all other buildings in the Jewish cemetery.[4]

Crowded together in the Ghetto, an average of thirteen

people to one room,[5] were Orthodox Jews, atheists, re-
cently baptized Christians and the Catholic children of
baptized Jews, twice-a-year religionists, Zionists of all
types, Communists, Socialists, big and little capitalists,
workers, artisans, *Luftmenschen,* refugees, philanthropists,
gangsters, assimilated Jews who neither spoke nor read
Yiddish, Hasidim with their eyes fixed on Heaven, engineers, doctors, lawyers, social workers, priests. And in this
mish-mash there was one thing in common—the Shield of
David, the yellow patch. No matter what it was called, it
distinguished them from the rest of the population as Jews,
a people bearing the mark of their inevitable destruction.[6]
Everyone wore it, for death awaited those who went without it. It was a potent factor in keeping them effectively
subdued. Fearful of the unknown but certain terror that
was outside the Ghetto, the vast majority resigned themselves to the expected medieval miseries within the walls.

Imbued with a fatal sense of history, the Ghetto dwellers
began the re-organization of their lives. Within the walls
developed a distorted mirror-image of the world outside.
The main task was to keep alive. The only economic con-
nection with the outside was the importation of food and
raw materials to be worked on in the Ghetto shops and
then exported via the official exchange station. Workers
fought for places in the large shops, such as those of Toeb-
bens and Schultz, to assure themselves of a fixed income
and exemption from forced labor. Other Jews, who had
managed to bring in with them foreign currency, jewels,
rare stamps, books or other valuables, and those who had
hidden stores of raw materials traded their possessions
through intermediaries for food and money. New indus-
tries developed in the Ghetto; the displaced manufactur-
ers, engineers and chemists set up dye works, tanneries,
textile plants, even a cigarette factory.[7] "From sugar, with-

out cocoa or nuts, they made almond chocolate."[8] In cellars, in every available nook and cranny, women and children made toys, dolls, brushes, mattresses, blankets, whatever the traditional sweat-shop could produce.[9] The everyday machinery of life creaked along, breaking down intermittently under the impact of the Nazi decrees. The Ghetto was a vast work-shop for the Germans and yet, because of the constant influx of refugees and deportees, there was mass unemployment.

In the "points," asylums for the displaced and homeless, misery was the order of the day. Here the Jewish community took upon itself its traditional duty of helping the helpless in the same way it had in the past ironically "better" days, but on a larger scale than ever before. Relief organizations did what they could to mitigate the general distress. In the words of Dr. Emanuel Ringelblum, the underground archivist of the Ghetto, "Through the active and generous aid of the American Joint Distribution Committee a large web of institutions for communal welfare was spread throughout Warsaw . . . conducted by the Jewish Society for Social Welfare, the Central Organization for the Protection of Children and Orphans, and the Society for the Protection of Health of the Jewish population. . . . Tens of thousands of adults and children were able to survive for a longer period because of the help of these institutions and of the ramified network of House Committees which cooperated with them."

Behind the brick wall surmounted by broken glass, the Jews were visited again with the quadruple Biblical curse of death by pestilence, by the sword, by wild beasts, and by famine. Epidemics swept through the Ghetto. Dysentery followed typhus and typhus followed dysentery. Tuberculosis, always a hidden threat, now became an open menace. Shootings were a daily event, sometimes "for cause"—

removing the yellow patch, forgetting to remove the hat
when speaking to a member of the Master Race, smuggling
food, and sometimes without cause, for the sake of "amusement"—every red-headed boy, every fifth woman, any
random target. But one plague was widespread—starvation.
Hunger pervaded every moment of the day for workers
and officials; it *was* the whole life of the homeless and
jobless. The Ghetto songs were those of hunger, the poems
were of hunger, the tales were of hunger. Hunger was
feared even more than the unpredictable Nazi decrees.

2. Famine in the Ghetto

THE GERMANS, IN ACCORDANCE WITH THEIR PLAN FOR EX-
termination of the Jews, instituted an incredibly irra-
tional rationing system. For Warsaw, the official ratio was
4:2:1 for Germans, Poles, Jews,[1] but actually even rationed foods were hard to come by, their importation into
the Ghetto being dependent on the whims of the Nazis.
Dr. Fischer, the governor of the Warsaw district, rejoiced
at the setting up of the Ghetto thus, "The Jews will disap-
pear because of hunger and need, and nothing will remain
of the Jewish question but a cemetery."[2] The Germans
made no attempt at concealment of their aims. An official
order, for example, dated April 19, 1941, states that "the
basic provisioning of the Jewish Residential District must
be less than the minimum necessary for preserving life,
regardless of the consequences."[3]

The great number of "illegals," unregistered Jews, the
refugees and deportees from all over Poland, and the official requisitions diminished the supply of food available to
any one individual. Stephen Starzynski, the mayor of Warsaw, was ordered to stop the distribution of food to the

Jewish district; he refused and, for this refusal, was sent to
a concentration camp in Germany, where he died.[4] The
Warsaw City Council, now filled with Nazi collaborators,
announced that, in spite of existing Polish law, it would no
longer supply bread to the patients in the hospitals; the
burden was thrown on the Jewish Community alone.[5]

Were it not for ample documentation no one would
believe how low the official ration was. The ration card for
October 1941 allotted 300 calories per day. In 1942, the
allotment was as follows per week:

> Bread: for Poles—49 oz.; for Jews—15.7 oz.
> Meat: for Poles— 8 oz.; for Jews—nothing
> Sugar: for Poles— 9 oz.; for Jews—1 oz.
> Fats: for Poles— 2 to 4 oz.; for Jews—nothing[6]

Dr. Hirszfeld estimated that the daily caloric intake in the
Ghetto was for employees of the *Judenrat*, 1500 calories;
for workers and professionals, less than 1000; for all others,
less than 300.[7]

The low caloric intake was only part of the picture. To
get food something else had to be sacrificed. The cost of
living (using July 1939 as a base of 100) rose to 433 one
year later and to 1293 the following year.[8] Food prices on
the black market during the first half of 1941 were as follows, per kilogram:[9]

	January	June
Rye bread	3.45 zlotys	18.15 zl.
Corn bread	5.00	27.60
Groats	8.00	25.00
Beans	6.50	29.95
Sugar	9.20	35.80
Potatoes	1.20	6.75
Horse Meat	5.00	20.30
Lard	15.50	72.30

By the end of 1941, horse meat sold for 30 zlotys per
kilogram.[10] Potato peelings sold for 3 zlotys per kilogram

until the Germans forbade their sale for "health reasons."[11] When the Ghetto was first closed, milk was permitted to be brought in for children less than five years of age; later it was allowed only for those less than a year old, and still later was completely forbidden.[12]

Most Jews could not afford to buy food on the black market and often could not even pay for the miserable amount rationed to them. It was estimated that to avoid dying of hunger a family of four needed 1120 zlotys a month as a minimum to pay for illegally acquired food in addition to the legal ration, which cost 300 zlotys. Sixty per cent of the Ghetto population depended for sustenance on the rationed food or on the community soup kitchens.[13] The luckier workers had for their breakfast black *ersatz* coffee with a thin slice of bread and for their mid-day meal again a slice of bread and a bowl of thin potato soup.[14]

Conditions never improved. On February 25, 1941, the *Gazeta Żydowska* (*Jewish Gazette,* published in Polish, the only newspaper the Germans allowed the Jews to read), printed a decree: "It is forbidden to sell any type of food to Jews outside the boundaries of the Jewish Residential District in Warsaw or to give or cede goods in any other manner."[15] Mary Berg noted in her diary on February 28, "The shortage of food is becoming more and more acute. One gets very little on the official ration cards and in the black market a pound of bread now costs 10 zlotys. All the bread is black and tastes like sawdust."[16] On May 20, she notes:

In the vegetable wagons in the streets one sees only dirty turnips and old last-year's carrots. Next to them are wagons full of stinking fish—tiny little fish in a state of decay. A pound of them costs one zloty. These fish now constitute the most important article of food in the Ghetto. It is the only one that the Germans allow to be sold freely. Of course, meat, chicken and even real carp for the Sabbath are to be found. The bazaar on Leszno Street has everything one's heart desires—but chicken costs 20 zlotys a pound. Kosher meat and fish are even more exorbitant; only those who have a large cash reserve can afford such luxuries and very few such people remain in the Ghetto. . . . The communal kitchens are still open and there one can get a dish of soup consisting of hot water with a potato swimming in it for 30 groszy. The *Judenrat* also has a kitchen for its own employees where soup with gruel is served, but this costs one zloty. . . . Marmalade is made of carrots and beets with sweetening of saccharin. 'Honey' is made of yellow-brown molasses. . . . But a piece of bread with such honey is far beyond the reach of most people.[17]

The influx of deportees from the provinces further strained the resources of the community. The soup became thinner and the portions smaller. No garbage, no scrap of food was to be found; everything was eaten.[18] An open letter in the *Gazeta Żydowska* of July 23, 1941, complains that only one person out of ten gets anything at all for lunch and that only by special permission of the House Committee.[19] In the same month a glass of hot water with saccharin and a slice of bread cost 40 groszy; jelly made out of horse bones, 10 groszy a portion; fish cakes made of the tiny fish called "stinkies," 30 groszy, and with a slice of bread, 50 groszy; candy made of molasses and saccharin, 20 to 30 groszy a piece; sugar, 30 zlotys a pound.[20] On September 1, 1941, the *Gazeta Żydowska* published a decree cancelling lard rations for public institutions "because the Jews do not eat pork." In November 1941, what passed for butter sold for 40 zlotys a pound. Horses disappeared from the Ghetto. Some were used for food; the others were sold to avoid the necessity of feeding them because oats were used to make gruel for humans and "who would think of giving such a delicacy to a horse?"[21] The bread rations were lowered to 20 ounces a week at the end of

1941; this was reduced by one-fifth the following summer.[22]

An underground leaflet circulated in "Aryan" Warsaw at the beginning of 1942 summarizes the famine in the Ghetto thus: ". . . 50 per cent of the people are dying from hunger, 30 per cent are starving and 15 per cent are undernourished."[23] In February 1942, grain smuggled into the Ghetto was being milled secretly; the chaff was used as a special kind of flour to make black cakes that looked like pressed hay. Ground dried flounder was used as a spread on bread instead of fats. Horse sausage was a great delicacy.[24] In April 1942, one egg cost 7 zlotys and a kilogram of horse meat 35 zlotys.[25] Hunger reached such a pass that on July 29, a week after the "resettlement" program had started, the Germans used a fiendish method to ensure that they would get their daily quota of 5000 to 10,000 Jews without too much trouble; they announced that all those who reported voluntarily to the *Umschlagsplatz* (where the trains to the Treblinka death camp were loaded) would get extra food. A notice was posted, signed by Leikin, the head of the Jewish *Ordnungsdienst* (Police), saying, "I hereby give notice that all those who, in conformity with the order to present themselves for selections for resettlement, voluntarily appear on July 29, 30 and 31 for evacuation will receive 3 kilograms of bread and 1 kilogram of marmalade per person. Collection point and distribution center—Stawki Place, corner of Dzika Street."[26] The ruse was successful. Hundreds, driven to desperation by their hunger, flocked to the Station. Indeed, the Germans were so pleased that they extended the time in which the Jews could, of their own free will, get bread and marmalade. Needless to say, the promise was not kept; it would have been silly to feed people who were soon to be exterminated.

The rapid shrinkage of the Ghetto population did nothing to lessen the hunger. In August, a pound of bread sold for 12 zlotys, and the workers in the factories, for twelve hours of labor with only an hour of rest, got a quart of watery soup and a quarter-pound of bread daily.

The mortality was frightful. Dr. Hirszfeld reported, "I have known houses in which a third of the occupants have died of hunger in the course of three months. . . . The refugees were wiped out by starvation alone."[27] In his biography he tells of the arguments that went on about whether it was right to prolong the misery of poor children, orphans and others by treating their illnesses. He describes the pathetic complaint of one child, saved from a severe attack of dysentery—"Why didn't you let me die right away? I saw my father and mother die of hunger, and now I'll die, too."[28] Menachem Linder, a member of the Jewish Self Help, gathered some statistics in 1941 and 1942; he found that first the refugees died, then the poorest Ghetto dwellers; a greater proportion of men died than women or children.[29] In March 1942, about 35 per cent of the inhabitants of the Ghetto had hunger edema; some houses had a higher percentage, 73 per cent at 64 Zelazna Street, for example.[30] During the next month, between 500 and 600 Jews died daily of starvation alone.[31]

The scenes of the famine in the Ghetto have been graphically described by many observers on the spot, including the Nazis and their friends. Their inhuman gloating does not bear repetition.[32] Tragedy was everywhere: dead bodies lying in the streets, covered with papers, anonymous, for if their names were known the ration card would be taken away from their families; almost naked children sitting around apathetically against the walls, their bones sticking out through their parchment skin. Occasionally there was rejoicing—a feast, for three people, made out of a small piece of bread, cabbage, a head of cauliflower and one egg.[33] But such feasts were rare. More often this took place: "The door opened and a man looking like a maniac appeared on the threshold. He was half naked, his thighs and shanks were thin as a switch. . . . The dead body of a woman was lying on the floor . . . a skeleton in a transparent waxen bag. This was his mother."[34] At the funeral for the children from the Wolska Street orphanage, the other children from the home brought a wreath inscribed "To the children who have died of starvation—from the starving children!"[35]

Begging went on day and night, hunger driving the beggars to disregard the death penalty for violation of the curfew. "I looked out of my window and saw the wandering skeletons. . . . Most of them were children. . . . As time went on, there were fewer and fewer of them because they were shot down by the Germans or just died out."[36] They cried, "Give me one potato, one, one tiny little potato, a crust of bread, some water from cooked vegetables or turnips!"[37] A song popular among the beggar children was *Hots Rachmones* (*Have Pity*), in Warsaw Yiddish dialect,

> Have pity, have mercy, good people!
> Drop me a piece, a piece of bread,
> A tiny, tiny piece of bread,
> Only a few crumbs, some crumbs of bread!
> Have mercy, have pity, good people![38]

A man started to beg on Leszno Street; two weeks later, he was no longer standing, but sitting with his trousers rolled up to show his swollen legs; a few days later, he was at the same place, unable to move; then he died. The generations of beggars disappeared one after the other with accelerated speed; often they fell on the street, their bodies remaining there until in due time they were carted off to a nameless grave.[39]

Not everyone starved quietly. Individuals known as *khappers* (grabbers) appeared, for the most part children. When one of these saw someone with a parcel that looked like food, he grabbed it, tore it open, and started to eat. The *khappers* became so experienced that before his victim had a chance to look around, the *khapper* had already swallowed the food. They made no attempt to run away; lightning-quick, they stuffed the food in their mouths, unheeding the blows rained on them.[40]

Rubinsztajn, the famous jester of the Ghetto, made macabre jokes on the famine. He refused a ration card—"I lost my wife and children, so now I should beg Hitler for a ration card? Let him stuff himself to death with my sour bread and bitter marmalade. I can even let him have in addition a kilo of spoiled cabbage and a dozen saccharin tablets." A favorite gesture of his was to go over to a corpse, lift off the paper and ask, "Did you remember to turn in your ration card, comrade?"[41]

It should not be supposed that the Jews made no attempt to stem the mounting tide of deaths from starvation. The rationed provisions sent in by the Germans were distributed by the rationing office of the *Judenrat* under the direction of Abraham Gepner and S. Winter. The Self-Help groups did a tremendous job within the limits of their resources. Supervised by I. Rothenberg, they organized mills, bakeries, artificial honey factories and soup kitchens.[42] TOZ, the Jewish health organization, in addition to its medical clinics, public baths and children's homes, had communal kitchens serving at least one meal a day. In July 1940, such a meal consisted of a bowl of potato or cabbage soup and a tiny portion of vegetables; twice a week a small piece of meat was offered at a cost of 1.20 zloty.[43]

The nutritive value of the soup was very low, ranging between 170 and 200 calories per portion; it was made

mainly from oats, and on one such meal a day, of a liquid
so low in calories, it was impossible to live.[44] The amount
of food distributed in the kitchens naturally varied from
time to time depending on how much and what type of
provisions could be obtained, but there was never enough
for the needs; if there was no food provided, the kitchens
stayed closed for days or weeks; the two grams per person
per day that was calculated was seldom reached even when
they were open, because the personnel would hide some
of the food for their own starving families.[45]

Food parcels were sent into the closed Ghetto by relatives in other parts of Poland; this source of supply was
soon cut off by the rounding up and extermination of the
Jews in the provinces. Food parcels from neutral countries
were sometimes delivered to the Ghetto, but were most
often confiscated by the Gestapo. After the war with the
Soviet Union started, parcels from that area, that had
amounted to as much as 2000 daily at one time, [46] naturally stopped coming.[47] The food packages from America
were a great deal of help, but they too no longer came after
Pearl Harbor. Receipt of food from Sweden and Switzerland was prohibited by an order of the Postmaster in December 1941.[48]

The American Joint Distribution Committee, directed
by David Guzik and Isaac Gitterman, was the major source
of outside help until December 1941, by financing soup
kitchens and other agencies in the Ghetto. The Catholic
Caritas Agency sent in food for the converted Jews and
later for other Jews.[49]

An interesting development was the Toporol, a society
for the promotion of agriculture, a paradox in the urban
Ghetto where there was barely space for a blade of grass to
grow. This group of idealists tried to improve the nutri-
tional status of the Ghetto by growing vegetables. Every

available space was used. "Where the Hospital of the Holy Ghost used to stand there is now a broad field sown with the various vegetables."[50] Balconies and roofs were used to grow radishes and onions. Tomatoes, carrots, cabbage, even potatoes were planted on bombed-out sites, 450 in all.[51] How much was raised? No definite figures are available, but all the diarists and journalists of the Ghetto agree that very little was accomplished in the fight against the general starvation.

As a matter of fact, nothing seemed able to stop the spreading famine. Whatever was done was like building a wall of sand against the ocean. Certainly none of the usual measures of social assistance were of any value.

3. The Smugglers

IT IS OBVIOUS THAT THE JEWS WOULD HAVE DIED OUT IN A few months, as the German authorities wished, had they been forced to subsist on the officially allowed rations. But the will to live was strong and both German and Polish guards were bribable. Smuggling became a literally vital business in the Ghetto.

During the early months of the closed Ghetto, Polish workers were still allowed to enter to work in various shops and factories. They made a good living on the side by bringing in foodstuffs hidden in their clothes.[1] Streetcars for Poles ran through the Ghetto; they were forbidden to stop, but conductors and motormen would throw off sacks of food at previously arranged points.[2] Many Poles threw packages of food over the Ghetto walls. The *concierges* of the "Aryan" buildings bordering the Ghetto became big *entrepreneurs*. For example, on Siena Street some houses had courtyards that gave on Zlota Street, which was parallel to Siena; here there was only heavy barbed wire, no brick wall, and all through the night there was the coming and going of provisions in and other goods

№ 038944

LEBENSMITTELKARTE
KARTA ŻYWNOŚCIOWA

Gültig für den Monat Oktober 1941 — Ważna na miesiąc październik 1941

Kreis
miejscowość

Name
nazwisko

Wohnort
miejsce zamieszkania

Strasse
ulica

Nicht übertragbar — Bez praw odstąpienia
Bei Verlust kein Ersatz
W razie zagubienia duplikat wydany nie będzie!

KUNDENLISTENNUMMERN — NUMERY LIST KONSUMENTÓW

| I | Nr | II | Nr |
| III | Nr | IV | Nr |

Różne 47 | Paźdz. 41
Różne 46 | Paźdz. 41
Różne 45 | Paźdz. 41
B Chleb 12 | Paźdz. 41
B Chleb 11 | Paźdz. 41
B Chleb 10 | Paźdz. 41
Chleb 9 | Paźdz. 41

N Różne 48 | Paźdz. 41
N Różne 49 | Paźdz. 41
N Różne 50 | Paźdz. 41
B Chleb 15 | Paźdz. 41
B Chleb 14 | Paźdz. 41
B Chleb 13 | Paźdz. 41

Z Cukier 18 | Paźdz. 41
Z Cukier 17 | Paźdz. 41
Z Cukier 16 | Paźdz. 41

Z Cukier 19 | Paźdz. 41

N Różne 52 | Paźdz. 41
N Różne 51 | Paźdz. 41

N Różne 54 | Paźdz. 41
N Różne 53 | Paźdz. 41

Różne 42 | Paźdz. 41
Różne 41 | Paźdz. 41
Różne 40 | Paźdz. 41
Różne 39 | Paźdz. 41
Różne 38 | Paźdz. 41
N Mięso 23 | Paźdz. 41
N Mięso 21 | Paźdz. 41

Marmolada 30 | Paźdz. 41
A Marmolada 31 | Paźdz. 41
N Różne 37 | Paźdz. 41
N Różne 36 | Paźdz. 41
N Różne 35 | Paźdz. 41
F Mięso | Paźdz. 41
F Mięso 20 | Paźdz. 41

Marmolada 28 | Paźdz. 41
A Różne 32 | Paźdz. 41
Różne 33 | Paźdz. 41
Różne 34 | Paźdz. 41

N Różne 56 | Paźdz. 41
N Różne 55 | Paźdz. 41

A ration card. (Jewish Historical Museum, Warsaw)

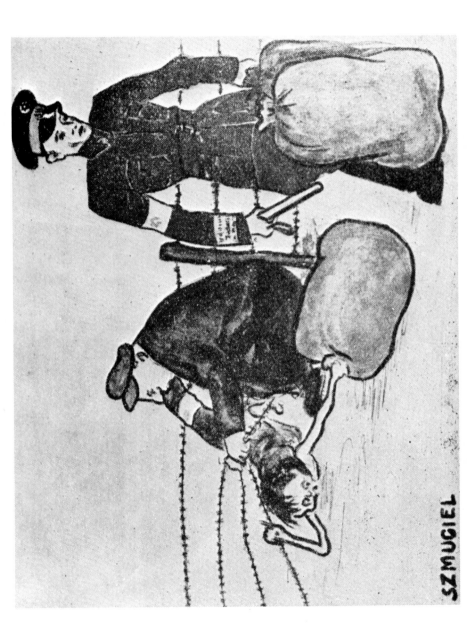

Smuggling over the wall. (*Jewish Historical Museum, Warsaw*)

Smugglers. (*Jewish Historical Museum, Warsaw*)

A smuggler captured. (*Jewish Historical Museum, Warsaw*)

Ghetto sketches: A *khapper*. (*Jonas Turkow*)

Ghetto sketches: Starving children. (*Jonas Turkow*)

Ghetto youth. (*Jewish Historical Museum, Warsaw*)

"Have pity!" (*Jewish Historical Museum, Warsaw*)

Ante mortem. (*Jewish Historical Museum, Warsaw*)

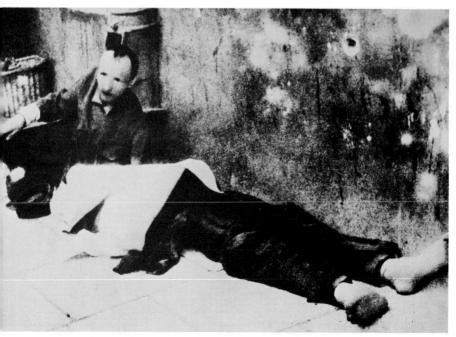

The dead and the dying. (*Jewish Historical Museum, War-saw*)

Dead from starvation. (*Jewish Historical Museum, Warsaw*)

Volunteers for marmalade—and death. (*Jewish Historical Museum, Warsaw*)

The "resettlement" notice. (*Jewish Historical Museum, Warsaw*)

Aufruf

An die Einwohner des jüdischen Wohnbezirks.

Gemäss Anordnung der Behörden vom 22. Juli 1942 werden alle Personen, welche nicht in Anstalten und Unternehmen tätig sind, unbedingt umgesiedelt.

Die Zwangsaussiedlung wird ununterbrochen weitergeführt. Ich fordere erneut die der Aussiedlung unterliegende Bevölkerung auf, sich freiwillig auf dem Umschlagplatz zu melden und verlängere auf weitere 3 Tage, d. h. den 2., 3. und 4. August 1942 die Ausgabe von 3 kg. Brot und 1 kg. Marmelade an jede sich freiwillig meldende Person.

Freiwillig zur Abreise erscheinende Familien werden nicht getrennt.

Sammelpunkt für Freiwillige: Dzika 3 — Stawki 27.

Der Leiter des Ordnungsdienstes

Warschau, den 1. August 1942

Wezwanie

Do Mieszkańców Dzielnicy Żydowskiej.

Zgodnie z zarządzeniem Władz z dnia 22 lipca 1942 r. przesiedleniu ulegną wszystkie osoby, nie zatrudnione w instytucjach i przedsiębiorstwach.

Przymusowe wysiedlanie będzie kontynuowane bez przerwy. Wzywam ponownie ludność, podlegającą wysiedleniu, do dobrowolnego stawienia się na Placu Przeładunkowym, przyczem przedłużam na dalsze 3 dni, t. j. na 2, 3 i 4 sierpnia 1942 r. wydawanie na każdą dobrowolnie zgłaszającą się osobę po 3 kg chleba i 1 kg marmolady.

Zgłaszające się dobrowolnie rodziny nie będą rozłączane.

Punkt zborny dla ochotników: ul. Dzika 3—Stawki 27.

Kierownik Służby Porządkowej

Warszawa, dnia 1 sierpnia 1942 r.

Druckerelbetrieb J. Bahman, Zagrebanej 6

The marmalade notice. (*Jewish Historical Museum, Warsaw*)

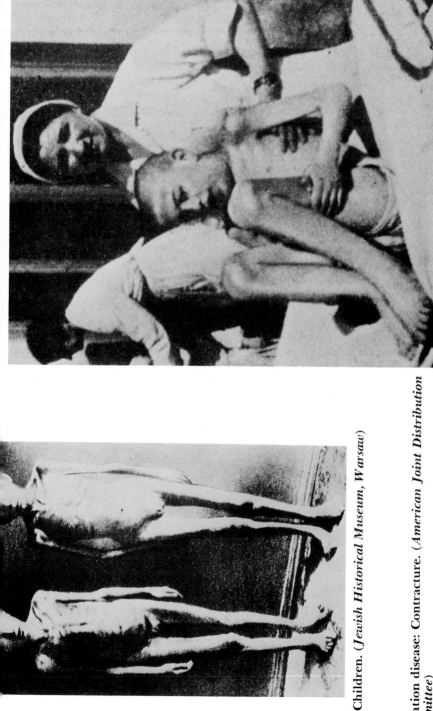

Children. (*Jewish Historical Museum, Warsaw*)

Starvation disease: Contracture. (*American Joint Distribution Committee*)

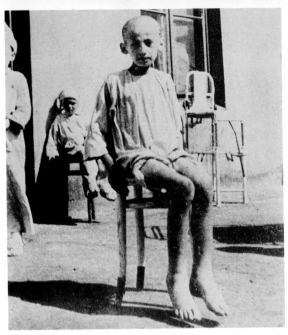

Starvation disease: Edema of the legs. (*American Joint Distribution Committee*)

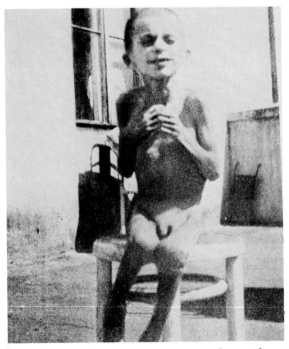

Starvation disease: Flexor contracture and muscle atrophy. (*American Joint Distribution Committee*)

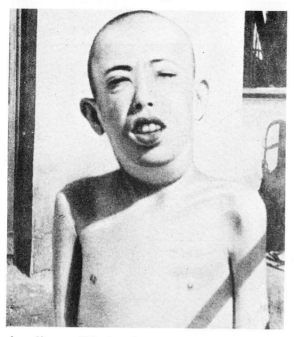

Starvation disease: "Nephrotic type" edema of face and neck. (*American Joint Distribution Committee*)

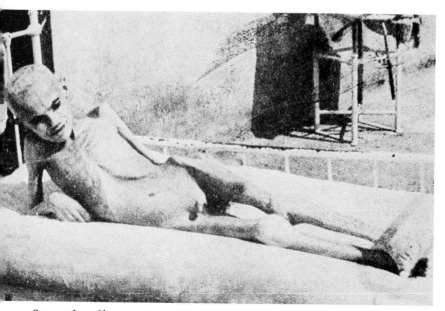

Starvation disease: "Dry" cachexia. (*American Joint Distribution Committee*)

Starvation disease: Atrophy. (*American Joint Distribution Committee*)

out. Bread, vegetables, sugar, butter, cheese were brought in in this manner "for sale at very high prices, of course, because people have risked their lives to get these things."[3] A large amount of wheat grain was imported in the same way through a similar courtyard on Leszno Street in December 1940.[4]

The hunger was so acute that men fought to get on the trucks that carried the workers out for forced labor outside the Ghetto walls. A day's unpaid, hard, unremitting physical labor, accompanied by beatings and the prospect of possible death at the hands of the taskmasters, was little enough to exchange for the chance to smuggle in some extra bread or a few potatoes.[5]

The ingenuity of the smugglers was amazing. Garbage collectors carried out garbage and brought back food in presumably empty wagons. Those collectors who had horses were exceptionally fortunate. They had passes for two horses. They would take only one out and bring in two by another gate, thus providing horse meat for the Ghetto, a real luxury.[6] A clever method for importing milk was used for a time in a building on the Ghetto border, on Franciszkanska Street; milk was poured into a pipe that ran across a street from the roof of a house on the "Aryan" side to a rooftop in the Ghetto.[7] The undertakers operated little hand-carts; under the corpses brought to the Jewish cemetery just outside the Ghetto they hid articles to be exchanged; in the cemetery these would be bartered for food with their Christian counterparts who worked in the adjoining Christian cemetery. In this way, whole calves and loads of potatoes were brought in.[8] The peak was reached one day when 26 cows were transported in this manner.[9] The food was concealed under straw and in the coffins that had held victims of typhus or of other diseases. This made no difference to the famished—starvation overrode any squeamishness.[10] Traffic went on through the sewers, too. Smugglers made their way in the noisome filth to the "Aryan" side where Polish confederates would hand them down packages and sacks of food through the manhole openings in exchange for jewels, currency or other articles of value. Some houses situated on the borders of the Ghetto, bombed out in the siege of Warsaw, had communicating cellars that extended as far as five houses under and past the Ghetto confines; these were naturals for smuggling. Small packages were passed through holes in the walls made by the removal of one readily replaceable brick.

The Germans were fully aware of the smuggling that went on and accepted it as a normal procedure at the same time as they took vigorous measures to combat it. Dr. Hagen, the medical officer for the General Government of Poland, when asked to allow milk to be brought in for infants, angrily replied, "How dare the Jews make such a proposal when they can supply all their needs with contraband?"[11] The death penalty established for illegal commerce with Jews did not deter the Poles from supplying the smugglers nor did the public execution of two men and six women in the Ghetto stop the Jews from trying to outwit the Germans. There was no other way to satisfy the needs of the population.

The smugglers themselves were not thought of as lawbreakers by the Jews, but rather as businessmen engaged in very speculative enterprises. There was no question about the risk. Dr. Ringelblum describes a scene on Leszno Street; "The head of a Jew is thrust through a hole in the basement of the gutted post-office building. Six guards see him, call over two Jews, and order them to pull him out. They do it, receiving a blow from the guards in the act. They order the smuggler to crawl back into his hole again

and, as he crawls, pierce his head with their bayonets."[12]
Against the possibility of losing their merchandise or their
lives were balanced the enormous profits of the business.
For example, even after paying off the German and Polish
guards, and the Jewish police, to a total of 19,000 zlotys,
one partnership of four smugglers made 16,000 zlotys in
one week. There were all sorts of unusual expenses, however. If a wagon was confiscated and the driver luckily sent
to prison, the smugglers' informal guild supported his family and tried to buy his freedom; if he was killed, the family was maintained as long as possible. They even set up a
mutual insurance company to pay for confiscated goods.[13]
Lured by the tremendous profits, by the prospect of getting enough money to get forged "Aryan" identification
cards to escape from the Ghetto, by the feeling that smuggling was getting back at the Germans, hundreds joined in
the traffic in contraband. And hundreds were caught and
killed on the spot. Nevertheless, smuggling went on until
almost the very end of the Ghetto period. The smugglers,
often hailed as saviors, had great prestige in the Ghetto.
An inhabitant of the Ghetto wrote: "In Kozla Street, in
Biala Street and in Siena Street, memorial plaques should
be put up with the inscription—'To all the quiet unafraid
heroic smugglers—honor them!' There will be no memorial plaques; no one will consider that. I know that greater
deeds of heroism took place. But in spite of that, Smugglers, I honor you!"[14] A prominent physician concurred
with this woman's opinion:

The walls of the Warsaw Ghetto, covered with broken glass,
had one and only one purpose; that was mass murder by general starvation. That was the essence of the plain and ugly
wall made of bricks and glass. Those who had the wall built
were fooled. Against this construction of the enemy arose an
unforeseen force—smuggling. This force which developed on
the pathologic base of a closed Ghetto became a paradoxical

phenomenon of our life. Smuggling, in principle a negative action, became for us a real blessing. The whole day long, as well as at night, this force was in constant motion, battling incessantly against the fiendish plan of the creators of these walls. Smuggling checked the famine, controlled its speed, its universality, the scope of its murderous action. The enemy fought against the smuggling by strengthening the brick walls, trying to seal the Ghetto off more completely. In vain! Nothing changed the situation! The enemy could not defeat the smugglers. The walls were always permeable. . . . The smuggler, the 'criminal', by his sweat and blood made our work and our very existence possible. . . .[15]

No matter how much food the smugglers brought in, it was quickly snapped up by the Ghetto population, at least by those who could afford the high prices. But there was another even more widespread special group of smugglers, not engaged in business, often the sole suport of their entire families. These were the little children from five to ten years of age. They travelled alone or in gangs. The smallest and most emaciated of them wrapped burlap bags around their bony little bodies and crawled through the barbed wire or were hoisted over the walls; the bigger ones acted as look-outs. Hiding in alleyways on the "Aryan" side, they made their way to more outlying districts, begging, buying or stealing food.[16] Death on discovery awaited them no less than for the adults, but more humane policemen contented themselves with merely giving the children severe beatings.[17] Dr. Hirszfeld tells of two instances he saw: a German guard took aim and deliberately shot a child in the legs, then shrugged his shoulders and remarked, "One smuggler less"; another turned a child around and calmly shot him between the shoulders.[18] To be shot to death was a chance that had to be taken; the choice was between that and starving to death. The little nameless heroes of the Ghetto went on with the only way

open to them. They brought in bread, flour and potatoes
to sustain their families a little while longer. Their deeds
were celebrated in a poem by Henrika Lazowert, one that
became widely popular in the Ghetto:

> Through walls, through holes, and through ruins,
> Through barbed wire I make my way.
> Hungry, thirsty, and barefoot,
> I slide through like a snake,
> At noon, at night, and at dawn,
> In the heat and hard summer rains.
> Envy me not my poor bundle—
> My life itself is at stake.[19]

4. The Czysta Hospital

THE HOSPITAL

Against starvation physicians had no remedy other than food, and that was not to be had. All they could do was study the famine-stricken. Dr. Ringelblum dryly notes on June 26, 1942, "Jewish physicians and professors are conducting scientific investigations. One of the most interesting subjects is hunger. Interesting because it is the most widespread disease in the Ghetto. . . ."[1]

The doctors had been treated no better than the rest of the Jewish inhabitants of Warsaw. Neither had their hospital. At the beginning of 1940, the Jewish Hospital (called the Czysta Hospital, after its location on Czysta Street) consisted of eight modern buildings, well-equipped, with 1490 beds and a hospital personnel of 147 physicians, 59 internes, 119 nurses plus student nurses, 13 bacteriologists and six pharmacists. The Children's Hospital on Sliska Street had 220 beds with 64 doctors and nurses.[2] A Polish superintendent, placed in charge of the Czysta Hospital by the Germans, a drunkard, totally uninterested in the operation of the hospital, did not object when the Germans confiscated all the drugs, sera and canned provisions.[3] From the Children's Hospital they took soap, ether and all prepared medications; seven doctors who protested against the removal of all the condensed milk were arrested for impudence.[4]

The Ghetto was established in November 1940, but the Czysta Hospital, despite its being on the "Aryan" side, was still allowed to function, to take care of Jewish patients.[5] There were constant rumors about its removal until in December 1940, there came an order that it must be closed and all the patients moved into the Ghetto. The *Judenrat* tried to have the order put off until the spring, when the weather would be more favorable, but were unsuccessful. No suitable place for a centralized hospital could be found. It was necessary to split it up into various units. All the fixed equipment had to be left behind, as well as much of the movable apparatus.

The surgical and roentgenological sections were set up at 1 Leszno Street, in the building formerly occupied by the Polish State Tobacco and Liquor Monopoly. The gynecologic and obstetric sections were transferred to the clinic building of Dr. Frishman at 5 Tlomackie Street. Respiratory diseases were treated at the former quarantine station on Zelazna Street. The school buildings at 6-8 Stawki Street and 80 Żelazna Street were used for infectious diseases, internal medicine, and miscellaneous specialties. The pharmacy, sterilization and disinfection units were located at 12 Elektoralna Street in the only remaining wing of the bombed-out, burned Hospital of the Holy Ghost. During the typhus epidemic of 1941, 109 Leszno Street was requisitioned for use as a branch of the hospital. Later, after much alteration and reconstruction, 21 Stawki Street was taken over for internal medicine and infectious disease; biochemistry and bacteriology laboratories were organized there, and an institute of pathology.[6]

The hospital had to start from scratch when it came to supplies. The *Judenrat* levied a special hospital tax of 10 groszy per day on every Jew and collected linens, clothing and instruments.[7] Medical equipment was later permitted to be sent in from Switzerland.[8] Drugs were procured at a high price through the firm of Kohn and Heller, Jewish collaborators who had a monopoly on the importation of medicines.[9] In the middle of 1941, the hospital was enlarged by the addition of 200 beds; funds for this purpose were collected by 3000 volunteers who raised the entire sum in one week. In addition the mattress-makers, through their guild, gave 200 mattresses worth 20,000 zlotys. At the beginning of 1942, 400 more beds were added, and still there was no room for all the sick.[10]

Patients lay on mattresses and cots in the corridors. The hospital became a pest-house, not a place of healing. The water pipes froze; there was no heat. The typhus epidemic caused further crowding so that the contagious cases could not be properly isolated. The shortage of bed linens, indeed of everything, aggravated the situation. Unsanitary conditions increased to such an extent that one doctor put out a mimeographed leaflet attacking the Ghetto administration for its neglect of the hospital.[11] Even after the epidemic had subsided and the most obvious evils had been corrected, the hospital mortality was high—because of hunger. Food was provided only by the official ration card; without any other source of supply, the hospital had to rely on the allotment sanctioned by the number of ration cards it had at any one time. Dr. Stein, the director of the hospital, complained bitterly in 1941, "The hospital has ceased to be a hospital; it is not even a poor-house. All the patient finds there is medical assistance which, in most cases, operates with very inadequate means. The food supply . . . is strictly a fiction. The daily ration of about 700 calories cannot sustain the organism. . . . The patient who has no means of providing his own food becomes swollen with hunger and soon dies—unusual progress in the history of medical treatment!"[12]

The doctors and hospital administrators did the best they could, gradually bringing the hospital back to a semblance of its former glory, but a murky semblance. They believed that the ruthless attitude of the Germans would change; they hoped that once more life would be orderly and safe. Everyone was totally unprepared for the events of July 1942. On July 20, almost all the doctors of the Czysta Hospital were locked up in the Pawiak prison,[13] held as hostages to ensure the carrying out of the deportation order. The pertinent sections of the order of July 22 follow:

Order of Deportation Notice
1. All Jewish inhabitants of Warsaw, regardless of age or sex, will be resettled in the East.
2. The following categories are exempt from resettlement:

. . .

(f) all Jews belonging to the personnel of the Jewish hospitals as well as all those enrolled in the Jewish Sanitary Columns;
(g) all Jews, members of the immediate families of persons enumerated under (a) to (f); only wives and children are considered members of families;
(h) all Jews who on the first day of resettlement are in one of the Jewish hospitals and are not fit to be discharged; *the unfitness for discharge must be attested by a doctor appointed by the Judenrat.* . . .

The following instructions for the duration of the resettlement are given to the *Judenrat;* for their carrying out the members of the *Judenrat* are responsible with their lives:

. . .

3. On July 23, 1942, the *Judenrat* is to evacuate the Jewish
   Hospital on Stawki Street and is to transfer the patients
   and staff to another suitable building inside the Ghetto so
   that by the evening of July 23, 1942, the hospital may be
   ready to receive daily the Jews to be resettled. . . .[14]

The infectious patients were sent to 80 Żelazna Street.
The remaining patients and the laboratories were moved
to 1 Leszno Street. Patients were carted by wagons and
rickshaws or walked in their slippers to the new loca-
tions.[15] The Germans lived up to their promise not to
disturb the hospital staffs or the patients—for a little while
at least. The hospital became a place of refuge for various
notables, brought on a variety of pretexts from the
Umschlagsplatz; among them was the world famous religious leader, Rabbi Hillel Zeitlin. Their hiding place did
not last long, only until the great "kettle" of September,
the mass round-up of Jews just before the cessation of
deportations.[16]

At that time the doctors were ordered to turn over the
hospital patients for deportation. Many parents and close
relatives of the hospital personnel were registered as patients to save them from Treblinka. Rather than see them
go off to be gassed, a group of doctors gave morphine injections to their old parents to give them an easy and quiet
death and a decent burial; the mothers of fifteen doctors
died in this manner.[17] The hospital administration did
not cooperate with the Germans in supplying deportees;
they felt it was the duty of the medical profession to keep
people alive, not select them for execution. Towards the
end of the September "action," therefore, the Germans
used a bitter stratagem. The hospital was told to move
back to Stawki Street. "This was taken as a sign by certain
people that the deportation was finished. But after only a
few days, all the 800 patients and 50 of the hospital personnel were loaded on the freight cars for Treblinka."[18]

After that, the hospital was cut down still further. 109 Leszno Street became a *DuLag* (*Durchgangslager*), a shaping-up hall for brush-workers. From Stawki Street the rest of the hospital was moved to 6-8 Gensia Street, a former warehouse, where a total of 200 physicians and other personnel were given *Lebensrechtsmitteln* (right-to-live cards) as people necessary for the Germans. 400 beds were set up for all the remaining Jews in the Ghetto and the workers in the shops. Some doctors were ordered by the S.S. to work on the "Aryan" side; others became plant physicians; others were deported as unneeded.[19] The hospital tottered along until January 1943. Its functioning was fitful and disorganized. Hospital workers came irregularly because they feared to go out on the streets where capture for forced labor or capricious shooting was common.[20]

The penultimate liquidation occurred on January 18, 1943. Bunkers, underground hiding places, had been constructed all over the Ghetto in anticipation of further deportations. The hospital's bunkers had been fitted out in the sub-cellars. On that day, warned in advance, the nurses took down as many patients as the bunkers could hold. Those unable to be moved and the children were left upstairs; the hospital administration, optimists to the last or else firm believers that all men had human feelings, felt that the sick children would be safe from the Germans. They were mistaken. The Germans shot in their beds all those unable to walk, including the children, and all the patients in the infectious disease section. The others, despite the bitter cold, were loaded into open trucks and taken away to the *Umschlagsplatz*. Some doctors committed suicide. The rest of the hospital personnel, those not hidden in the bunkers, were either also taken away or else killed on the spot.[21]

A hospital was again set up on the same site, in the last

stages of the Ghetto. It was no longer a general communal institution. It was maintained by volunteer workers trying to give what little comfort they could to the sick. After their rout on Nalewski Street on April 18, 1943, the beginning of the Warsaw Ghetto uprising, the Germans looked for an easy victory. The next day they occupied the hospital, killed all the patients and transported the medical personnel. The building was then blown up.[22]

THE DOCTORS

The daily life of the doctors was beset with the same horrors as the rest of the Ghetto population. The Germans treated all the Jews alike with no regard for education or degrees or honors. The doctors had no special privileges, other than temporary exemption from deportation.

There were about 600 Jewish doctors in Warsaw at the beginning of the war. As the Germans approached the city, some fled with their families to the East to find refuge in what was later to become the Soviet Zone. Some went with their army units to battle and were killed; others were taken prisoner and used by the Germans in the prisoner of war camps while they existed. About 200 were left in Warsaw when the city finally fell to the Germans.[23] The number stayed about the same for a time: Christians of Jewish ancestry were added and the Germans impressed others to treat their wounded after the war with the Soviet Union started in June 1941. Then, as with the rest of the population, typhus, tuberculosis, hunger and casual shooting took their toll and the number of doctors steadily decreased.

The same indignities inflicted on other Jews were borne by the doctors, and a few special ones added. On December 10, 1939, mass arrests of the Jewish intelligentsia began;[24] release was effected by the payment of ransom, in the form of fines, but the lawyers and physicians were kept in prison longer than the others. When the General-Government (German-occupied Poland, other than those areas incorporated into the Reich) was established, the title of "physician" was not allowed to be used by Jews; they were to be known as "Krankenbehändler"—tenders of the sick. It followed that they lost all their pension rights and positions in the Civil Service and official hospital posts. On March 6, 1940, Jewish doctors were forbidden to treat "Aryans" because, as the *Krakower Zeitung* explained on March 12,[25] "Jewish doctors spread typhoid and typhus fevers" because Jews are by nature dirty and because they want to infect the Gentile population. The doctors wore Red Cross bands to serve as notice to the guards that they had permission to be out on the streets after the curfew to visit patients. Guards occasionally pretended not to see the bands and shot them for sport. There were other less mortal punishments. A doctor who allowed the Red Cross band to slip down over the yellow Shield of David was beaten and fined.[26] Doctors who rode the street-car to the hospital on Czysta Street, before its removal into the Ghetto, were taken off and forced to do calisthenics for an hour for the amusement of the Germans.[27]

Amidst danger and debasement the physicians in the Ghetto carried on their work. As noted above, they reorganized the hospitals and set up a public health administration under the *Judenrat*. They too, like everyone else in the Ghetto, tried to bring normality into the insanity of their existence. Private practice was carried on to some extent and with great limitations. Prescriptions could not be written for the most indispensable drugs because it was precisely these drugs whose importation into the Ghetto was forbidden. Indeed even those pharmaceutical preparations permitted to be brought in were limited in amount by order of the German authorities.[28] Professional protocol was strictly observed, as evidenced by the style of the acknowledgments given in the articles written for the research project on starvation and the careful maintenance of the hospital hierarchy. Mindful of the Hippocratic Oath, of their duty to teach and hand on their learning to a younger generation, the physicians of the Ghetto organized illegal medical courses. The professors were all noted Polish scientists, including Dr. Samuel Goldflam, the world renowned neurologist, Dr. M. Kocen, the famous hematologist, Dr. Michael Szejnman, and Dr. Bronislawa Fejginowna, the authority on bacteriophages. Among them also was Dr. Ludwik Hirszfeld, the bacteriologist, an intensely religious Catholic of Jewish origin, who escaped to the "Aryan" side during the mass deportations and was fortunate enough to survive the war. He later became Director of the University of Wroclaw. In his autobiography he has given a vivid description of the life in the Ghetto and in the hospital.

5. The Hunger Project

IN THE MIDST OF THE MASS STARVATION A GROUP OF DOC-
tors, on the initative of Dr. Israel Milejkowski, the head
of the Health Department of the *Judenrat,* decided to use
the horrors of their daily existence to advance medical science, a touching demonstration of faith that humane studies would survive the war. At that time, when to the best of
their knowledge, it appeared that Hitlerism was triumph-
ing, they refused to believe that the victory of evil would
be permanent. "Men without a future, with a final effort
of will, decided to make a modest contribution to the
future. When death struck some of them, those who remained continued their task, awaiting their own deaths,"
in a feverish attempt to complete their investigations.[1]

An Organizing Commission was set up in November
1941, to develop a plan of work, to find resources and to
make assignments. Dr. Julian Fliederbaum made a tenta-
tive outline of the investigations to be pursued. He en-
listed the help of the physicians in the Bauman-Berson
Children's Hospital so that simultaneous studies could be
carried on in both hospitals.

The working out of the research project was vigorously pursued. All sorts of obstacles, physical and psychological, had to be overcome. The laboratories were re-organized; some new instruments were purchased; cubicles were set aside for patients under study; by February 1942, all was in readiness, and the project formally got under way, although some preliminary work had already been done. Interim meetings to discuss the findings were held monthly up to the beginning of July. At that time a general conference was held to which were invited leading members of the *Judenrat,* including its presiding officer, Adam Czerniakow. The doctors had to convince the *Judenrat* officials who held the purse strings that the project had meaning. Dr. Milejkowski stressed the importance and the goals of the research; Dr. Fliederbaum and Dr. Apfelbaum gave summaries of the work done up to this point. In the animated discussion that followed, the doctors brought out the social significance, as well as the scientific value, of the project. The conference convinced the *Judenrat.* It gave permission to buy and smuggle necessary instruments into the Ghetto, although it had little money to allocate for such purchases.[2] Voluntary contributions were solicited; those who could give no money gave of their time and labor. The cubicles assigned for experiments were kept spotlessly clean; the floors shone; smoking was forbidden in the laboratories; no one wearing street shoes or rubbers was allowed to enter the special rooms. Blackboards were put up on the walls; graphs and charts were displayed to show the progress of each phase of the work. The statistical material was collated in a manner "that could not be bettered in the best universities in Europe," Dr. Hirszfeld said.[3]

Just when the studies were going full swing came the mass expulsion from the Ghetto on July 22, 1942. The work was suddenly interrupted. It was interrupted but not abandoned. The charts and tables, the so painfully gathered data, the rough drafts, as much as were available, were hurriedly gathered together and carefully hidden lest they be lost.

After the temporary cessation of the deportations to Treblinka, further studies were impossible. The necessary human material was lacking, gone up in ashes and smoke at the death camp. Whatever had been saved of the accumulated data was systematized and edited. This final stage was carried out in one of the buildings in the Jewish cemetery, an ironic touch. Those doctors still remaining in the Ghetto held meetings at the risk of their lives to decide what should be included in the manuscript. They had no hope that they themselves would survive to see its publication, but they went on with their labors, nevertheless, confident that future generations would find in the research on hunger an inspiration for scientific investigation.[4]

Shortly before the final liquidation of the Ghetto, the manuscript was smuggled out. It was entrusted to a woman, one of the many unsung heroines of the Ghetto who acted as liason with the "Aryan" side. She brought it to Professor Witold Orlowski, of the University of Warsaw, together with a letter from the editorial committee. Professor Orlowski says, "I did not ask her name. In those days knowledge of it might have been dangerous to her or to those who sent her." The letter asked him to preserve the material sent to him. He did so. After the Germans had been driven out of Warsaw, Dr. Apfelbaum reclaimed the typescript from its hiding place and readied it for publication, despite the fact that some articles were incomplete because of the disappearance of the authors and their notes.[5]

6. The Research

THE GHETTO DOCTORS WERE DRIVEN BY THEIR SCIENTIFIC zeal to utilize the great wealth of material available to them because at no other time in modern history had there existed such localized mass starvation in the presence of comparatively good medical facilities. True, studies on starvation had been done in World War I, but they had been limited in scope and many questions had been left unanswered: the riddle of the swellings found in hunger, the nature of the bony deformities, the problem of hemorrhages, the role of vitamins and the endocrine glands. The doctors set as their goal the answering of these questions.

In order to establish a norm in which non-essential deviations would be held to a minimum, infants, pubescent children, and the aged were excluded as subjects for the study, as were all cases of starvation complicated by tuberculosis and other diseases. Only "pure" starvation cases were examined. If the terminal autopsy showed that the "pure" cases were really "impure" because of superimposed infections, the findings were discarded.[1] No similar study had ever gone to such lengths to make a base line for its determinations.

CLINICAL FEATURES OF STARVATION
IN ADULTS

Nothing was too obscure or too trivial; nothing was overlooked in the investigators' searching descriptions of the course of starvation from the beginning to the final moment of death.

The first symptom of starvation was a dry mouth, accompanied by increased urination; it was not unusual to have patients with a daily excretion of more than four litres of urine. Then came a rapid loss of fat and a desire to chew constantly, even on inedible objects. These symptoms subsided as starvation progressed; even weight loss slowed down. The next group of symptoms were somatopsychic: Patients complained of general weakness, of being unable to carry out the simplest tasks; they became sluggish, lay down frequently, slept fitfully, and wanted to be covered up to combat the abnormal feeling of coldness. They lay in the characteristic fetal position, legs drawn up and shoulders hunched over, so that contractures of the flexor muscles often developed. They became apathetic and depressed. Even the sensation of hunger became dulled; yet when any type of food was seen, many grabbed at it and wolfed it down without chewing.[2]

Weight was from 20 to 50 percent lower than the prewar weight; it varied between 65 and 90 pounds. The lowest weight observed was in a 30-year-old woman—53 pounds.[3]

Bowel movements increased, often leading to a bloody dysentery, causing further weakness. Swelling appeared first in the face, then in the feet and legs; it later spread over the entire body; fluid often accumulated in the chest and abdominal cavities.

Very few patients complained of bone or joint pains. As a matter of fact, very few complained of anything other

than weakness. An even smaller number said they "felt
nervous," a surprising finding in view of the surroundings.
Gross mental breakdowns, the classic psychoses, were
rare.

The skin was pale and curiously pigmented over areas
traumatized by the scratching that went with a variety of
skin afflictions (scabies, pustulation, boils and louse bites).
A very thorough study was made by Dr. Raszkes of the
gross and microscopic features of the skin in starvation;
he was put to death at Treblinka and his detailed papers
were lost. Some were recovered, however; they demon-
strated a definite tendency to pigment accumulation under
the influence of minor injury. Even early and even in the
presence of swelling, the skin was dry and scaly. It became
thinned out, lost its elasticity and came to look like cigarette paper and feel like parchment, so that mere youths
took on the appearance of old men. The sebaceous glands
atrophied; acne and dandruff disappeared. In the summer,
sunburn to the point of blistering occurred rapidly; in
cold weather, chilblains were common. In the final stages
of starvation, the face became dirty-gray in color.

The nails became opaque, striated, often clawed. Infections of the nail-beds came on easily.

Body temperatures were uniformly lowered, the mean
being 96.8° F. Sometimes it dropped to 95.4° F. In infectious diseases such as typhus, where fever is usually very
high, there was only a slight rise. In tuberculosis the rise
was insignificant, thus often presenting a diagnostic problem.

Muscular weakness was so pronounced that it resulted in
slowness of movement even under conditions of stress. To
give one instance, a patient snatched a piece of bread from
a doctor and tried to run away with it, but he fell to the
ground, crying out, "My legs won't carry me!"[4] Creatine,

which appears in the urine as a rule only after great muscular effort, destruction of muscular tissue, or some endocrine disorders, was found in the urine of 17 out of 20 starving patients.

Eye examinations, done with great difficulty, gave surprising results. The patients, according to Dr. Fajgenblat, objected to the investigations and manipulations; most of the studies, those on visual acuity and fields of vision, are subjective and require good will as well as strict attention from the patients. Nevertheless, the visual apparatus of 20 female patients, none older than 30, was examined in great detail. Unfortunately, all the exact figures and the field of vision graphs were lost during the July 1942 expulsions. Enough data remained, however, to demonstrate that what was expected to be found was not there; *i.e.*, the signs of avitaminosis-A: keratomalacia, night-blindness, and Bitot's spots. No visual malfunction was found nor complained of, allowance being made for the presence of cataracts. The most striking finding was a bluish discoloration of the sclera, such as is usually found only in rare diseases associated with fragility of the bones, low blood calcium levels, and high excretion of calcium in the urine and feces. All these occur during starvation, other studies showed; they indicate a parathyroid dysfunction, avitaminosis-D being finally ruled out by still other studies. The pupillary reactions were sluggish, interpretable as a slowing up of the neuromuscular reaction or as weakness of the iris muscles. Almost without exception, the patients showed lens opacities resembling those in early senile cataracts, with the opacity increasing proportionately to the age of the patient. The intra-ocular pressure in all the patients was lowered, even down to 12 mm. Hg. (normal is 20-28 mm.). The starving patient has low blood pressure; if the intra-ocular pressure remained normal, there would be great resistance to blood entering through the retinal artery, thus causing retinal disturbances; Dr. Fajgenblat felt that the lowered intra-ocular pressure was a defense mechanism against such changes, although he could not rule out hypo-adrenalism. The visual fields for light and the basic colors showed no departure from the normal. "Further investigations on adaptation to dim light could not be pursued because of technical difficulties."[5]

The auditory apparatus showed no changes. Hearing and equilibrium were undisturbed.

The tongue was often coated; the base was smooth, with atrophic papillae. Patients often complained of burning of the tongue. Tonsillar tissue was atrophied.

The teeth quickly became carious. Young people (20 to 25 years old) often had such advanced dental caries that they could barely chew their food.

As starvation progressed, the voice became hoarse. The cause was undetermined; it may have been organic, relating to weakness of the laryngeal muscles, or functional, due to the drying out of the mucous membranes of the larynx. In adolescent young men, the voice did not deepen.

Particular attention was paid to the lungs. It was found that hypotonia was constant; this finding was confirmed by X-ray and fluoroscopy in a few cases and by autopsy in most. Vital capacity was lowered greatly (to 1.5 to 3 litres) in studies made on 20 cases. The frequency of respiration was lowered to 11 or 12 a minute (normal is 18 to 20), and thus the volume of the respired air greatly diminished. The impaired elasticity of the lungs contributed greatly to the decrease in air exchange. Bronchitis and bronchopneumonia were common, as was tuberculosis (see below). Often, however, what was diagnosed clinically as pneumonia turned out to be, on autopsy, pneumonomalacia ending up in cavernous destruction of pulmonary tissue. Bronchial asthma was rare, as were all diseases of allergic origin.

The heart sounds were faint, with an occasional functional systolic murmur. The heart beat slowly and regularly, the mean being 40 to 50 beats per minute, the extremes 36 and 80. The arteries felt barely filled; pulse taking was consequently difficult. The peripheral veins were almost invisible. The blood pressure was greatly lowered: the systolic ranged from 60 to 100 mm. Hg. and the diastolic from 40 to 60 mm. Hg.

Since every part of the body is affected by starvation, it was not surprising that endocrine malfunction appeared. The changes in children will be described in the next section. Menstruation ceased in adult women; men became impotent. These obvious disturbances of the genital function were related also to the hair distribution, depending on the age of the patient. Starvation coincident with puberty caused increased hairiness of the head; hair rarely appeared around the sexual organs, and when it did, in females it took the form of an upright triangle (the normal male distribution) and in males the form of an inverted triangle (the normal female distribution). Long lashes and thick eyebrows occurred in both sexes. In girls and women a fine down appeared on the face, to the point of actual mustaches and sideburns; this down sometimes came out even on the eyelids. Young men were relatively beardless. In patients 20 to 50 years of age the hair was lost rapidly from the head, the axillae, and the genital areas. There was no evidence of the castration syndrome, however, in the eunuchoid form of abnormal growth of the lower extremities nor as abnormal deposition of fat.

Hypothyroid features (dry skin, low metabolism, etc.) were the norm in starvation. The parathyroid functioned on a greatly lowered level, shown by tests on neuromuscular activity and trophic changes in the teeth, skin and nails. Likewise, other examinations showed hypofunctioning of the adrenals and pituitary gland. Studies on sugar metabolism (see page 65) showed, however, normal activity of the endocrine portion of the pancreas. All in all, the doctors concluded that the energy-sparing hormones predominated over the energy-producing hormones.

Prolonged starvation changed youths into prematurely old men. "My strength fades away like a candle flickering out," one of them said. The apathy became more pronounced, sleep more prolonged, arousal less possible. The passage between life and death was very gradual, sometimes imperceptible. Death resembled the fading out of an old, old man. Pulse and respiration slowed up more and more. Finally all vital functions ceased. Death came silently.[6]

STARVATION IN CHILDREN

Apathy was the first symptom of starvation in children. They lost interest, stopped playing, became sluggish, cranky and whiny. Then they became very quiet; their intellectual development seemed to stop, even to retrogress. In more advanced stages they lay on their sides, hunched up, with bent knees, with blankets over their heads because they felt chilly, even in summer. They lay quietly, almost motionless, but they did not sleep. Most suffered from insomnia. In the very advanced stage they no longer were able to sit, much less walk.

Weight averaged about 50 per cent of the normal, taking into consideration the arrest of growth as well as the height. Although growth arrest was not so obvious as weight loss, it occurred in almost every child. Children from 2 to 5 and from 7 to 9 showed the greatest growth deficit; 3 and 4-year-olds were often no taller than infants and 9-year-olds no bigger than the usual 6-year-old. Among the older children starved during puberty the growth differential was not so great; they even appeared taller than they actually were because of their emaciation.

Body temperature was subnormal, rising only slightly in infectious diseases, in contrast to the usual high fevers seen in normal children with the same diseases. In tuberculosis, fever seldom appeared; very severe cases were observed often, with extensive destructive lesions, in which the temperature throughout was often normal or subnormal.

Skin changes varied. Sometimes the skin was pale and pasty looking; sometimes, cold and cyanotic. Most of the children had brown spots, usually at the site of old scars, or on the back, neck, abdomen, or in the skin creases or where clothing rubbed on the body. Sometimes there was pigmentation of the entire body. Pigmentary changes occurred mostly in those over five and those without edema. The skin became dry and scaly and lost its elasticity. Hairy growth was increased on the neck and on the face, appearing on the latter as sideburns.

Edema varied in the frequency of its appearance and its localization depending on the age of the children, being rare in those up to 2 years of age. Those from 2 to 5 showed the greatest tendency to edema; in older children dry cachexia was commoner. Swelling appeared mainly in the face and neck, becoming more quickly generalized the younger the child; it was always symmetric, its location varying with the position of the body, being greater in the dependent areas. Severe edemas led to hydrothorax, ascites, hydropericardium and swelling of the scrotum and labia.

The peripheral lymph nodes were felt as hard, painless, movable bean-sized masses; the atrophy of the subcutaneous tissues made them even more evident.

Parotid and submaxillary gland enlargement was a very characteristic sign often found in children with advanced cachexia; the parotids, especially, were greatly enlarged, although the ducts were unchanged. In all these cases the sublingual glands were not enlarged. Salivary secretion being very poor, it was felt that the enlargement was due to edema of the salivary glands but that the atrophy of the surrounding fatty tissue made them appear even larger.

The muscles were so weak and atrophied that the skin seemed to adhere directly to the skeletal structures. Children without swelling looked like skin-covered skeletons. The epiphyses of the long bones looked swollen, as in rickets; however, exact bony measurements and X-ray studies showed that these were apparent changes which had nothing in common with rickets. Muscle contractures were found in cases of extreme debility and included the flexor muscles of the thighs and legs and, to a lesser degree, the flexors of the forearms. Contractures were caused by the constantly bent extremities, the extreme passivity, and the muscular atrophy and the biochemical changes attributed to that atrophy. Sometimes there was limited motion at the hip, knee, and elbow joints without actual contracture. The contractures disappeared very slowly with a fuller diet; they occasionally lasted a long time after the child had seemingly recovered, thus making walking impossible. Some convalescents waddled in their gait despite a normal angle between the neck and the body of the femur, as shown by X-ray; the peculiar gait was probably due to over-relaxation of the muscles and ligaments.

The most interesting observation was the absence of

rickets. The only cases seen, and they were rare, were in 1942 in infants and 2-year-olds from a new group of deportees. During the entire period no case of late rickets was found. The X-ray pictures of the long bones were normal. In a few cases there was mild general decalcification, but the normal contours and growth lines were preserved. These observations contradict those made during World War I when rickets was very frequent and often appeared as rhachitis tarda, the late form, in older children and youths. The Ghetto infants all got prophylactic vitamin D, which was not used during World War I, but the doctors felt that such prophylaxis was not the only factor in the non-appearance of rickets. Scurvy, a sign of avitaminosis-C, was also absent, and there was no substitute for the vitamin given.

Dentition was faulty. The tonsils were small. The tongue was smooth.

The respiratory system showed pulmonary emphysema, especially in advanced cachexia, with a lessening of respiratory mobility and weak respirations. Fluid accumulations in the chest cavity were common, usually unilateral because the children lay constantly on one side.

The slow pulse, unusual in children, was typical of starvation, being as low as 55 to 60 per minute. It was often imperceptible, and faded out a long time before death actually occurred. Vascular collapse was indicated by the cyanotic coldness of the extremities, the barely visible superficial veins, and the tendency to thrombosis. It was not unusual to find faint heart sounds and irregular contractions. The highest blood pressure recorded was 60-65 mm. (systolic), much lower than the norm.

The blood usually showed only a mild anemia and a leukopenia, with a relative lymphocytosis. Noteworthy was the absence of eosinophiles even when intestinal parasites

were present. And equally noteworthy was the absence of
the hemorrhagic diathesis, which would ordinarily be expected with a diet so low in proteins and vitamins.

Diarrhea was one of the most common symptoms, coming on very early in the course of starvation. In some cases
it lasted throughout the entire period of observation; such
children usually died. The stools were frequent, semi-
liquid, and curdy; sometimes they resembled those of a
bloody colitis.

The gastric contents were analyzed in 15 children, fasting and after the giving of an alcohol-test-meal. Hypo-
acidity was found in every case.

No urinary disturbances were found, other than diure-
sis. No casts, hyaline or other types, were found in the
urine. Concentration and dilution tests were done in 25
cases. The amount of water eliminated exceeded the
amount taken in, a finding normal for well children, but
the elimination of water was generally slowed up; the
children passed urine as long as two hours after taking the
water, showing the slow passage of water through the body
tissues.

No neurologic changes were found, sensory or motor,
not even the expected peripheral neuritis.

In pubescent children sexual maturation was markedly
impaired, evidenced by the absence of pubic hair, menstruation, and breast development in all but a tiny minor-
ity of cases.

Tuberculosis took a virulent form in the starving children. It attacked not only the lungs, but also the perito-
neum and the intestinal tract, even the uterus in two girls
(proved by autopsy). Its course was violent and acute,
demonstrating the complete lack of reaction of the body.

The situation was totally different in children with
acute infectious diseases. Despite the great crowding in the
hospital, epidemics were rare and their intensity more and

more benign. At the beginning of 1940 an epidemic of chickenpox lasted about six months; almost all the children caught it, but in 1941, when a case of chickenpox appeared, no epidemic broke out and only two children got the disease out of 250 to 280. Only older children, in a wretched state of nutrition, were in the hospital at this time, but in other groups of children, relatively better nourished, chickenpox spread rapidly. The same thing was seen in measles, confirming the clinical impression previously held that measles attacks the well-nourished first of all. Measles occurred rarely and in non-epidemic form amongst the most poorly nourished groups; an extensive epidemic appeared in rather well-fed deportees from Germany. With the exception of one epidemic early in 1940, meningitis was also uncommon. The body reacted weakly to the contagious diseases, with insignificant eruptions and low fever. Thus, despite the barely marked symptoms, such diseases in these very enfeebled children ended fatally.

The weak body reaction was shown in another field. Allergic phenomena (serum reactions, bronchial asthma, rheumatic fever) were rarely found. Before the war, the end of the winter and the beginning of spring were marked by a very high percentage of cases of rheumatic fever in the Children's Hospital. In the first three years of the Nazi occupation there were only five cases, two of them recurrences of earlier attacks.

The course and the prognosis in starvation disease depended on the duration of starvation, the type of diet, the individual constitution, and the age of the child. The younger the child, the more poorly he withstood starvation; the greatest mortality was in infants, reaching close to 100 per cent. Edema was a bad prognostic sign, indicating almost certain death in most of the children under 5 or 6 years of age.[7]

PHYSIOLOGIC REACTIONS AND EXPERIMENTS

The foregoing clinical descriptions led to the conclusion that in starvation energy saving and parsimony was concurrent with the insufficiency of energy. The sparing of energy, however, is limited by the physiochemical laws by which life is governed. The basal metabolic level cannot be indefinitely depressed; an end-point is eventually reached. A healthy active person uses up about 3000 calories per day; the clinical material in the Warsaw studies was made up of individuals who lived on 600 or 800 calories a day, often much less. The caloric deficiency could only be made up by endogenous feedings; that is, by eating up their own tissues. It can be readily calculated that these patients should have lived only 60 to 75 days, and yet they survived for months and years longer.

What prolonged their lives? Only an energy economy different from that in the normal human being, an economy that resembled somewhat that in animals during a state of hibernation. The laboratory studies and experiments attempted to determine what new mechanism came into play to bring about such a dramatic sparing of energy. Repeated observations were made, checked and rechecked, and the findings summarized in charts and tables on a scale never before done in a study of this nature.

The most extensive investigations were done on the circulatory system.[8] Its function, to carry oxygen and nutritive elements to the tissues and remove the waste products of metabolism, was thoroughly studied. It was found that the arterial blood pressure was very low; the venous pressure was equally low. The velocity of the blood in the circulation was half of the norm. The capillary circulation was slowed. The minute-volume of the heart was

1.5 liters in contrast to the normal 8-10. There was an asthenia of the entire circulatory system, a peculiar weakness that showed itself in a failure to respond to stimulation, thus saving energy vitally needed to sustain life. For example, contrary to what takes place in a state of health or when the body is attacked by other diseases, there was no compensatory change in the circulation after change of body position, nor after physical effort, nor after drugs (adrenalin, caffeine, atropine), not even after increased protein intake (although two eggs more than the usual starvation diet could not exactly be considered a great increase). No functional cardiac neuroses were discovered, despite the environment of terror; pre-existing paroxysmal tachycardia disappeared.

Electrocardiograms showed a very slow regular rhythm, low voltage in all leads, no changes in the ventricular complex, flattening of the T wave in all leads, increased conduction time in the S-T segment, and no change after exercise. The last finding indicated the heart's rigidity in adapting, which, even at rest, was functionally insufficient and hypo-energetic.

And yet cardiac failure, in the usual sense, did not occur. Why? The Warsaw investigators, after a long and complex series of laboratory studies on capillary circulation, arterial and venous pressures and blood volume, concluded that the lessening of tissue combustion in the body lessened the work of the already malfunctioning heart. A balance was struck. The heart conserved its energy to make up for its inadequate nutrition. The blood still circulated, sluggishly, at a lower speed than previously, and yet sufficiently fast to prevent tissue death.

The blood itself was the subject of a number of studies, morphologic and functional, including examination of the bone marrow in a number of cases.[9] Here, too, the rigidity of response was noted: there was no increase in white cells such as usually occurs after a protein meal or in infectious processes nor was there any change in the sedimentation rate in superimposed acute or chronic infections. Anemia of varying degree was constant, with a reduction in the number of white cells, also. There was no evidence that the anemia was caused by increased blood destruction or by the dilution of the blood. It was found that the bone marrow was rich in cellular elements but that migration to circulating blood was impaired. Hemorrhages did not appear despite a low thrombocyte count.

Attempts were made to correct the anemia by various means: administration of iron, transfusions, liver injections, feeding of yeast, and increase in diet. The last alone had effect; more food was not available for the patients; the anemia persisted and became progressively worse. As the cachexia of starvation deepened, the bone marrow began to fail and eventually a state indistinguishable from aplastic anemia developed.

Laboratory studies were made on stomach functions. It was noted early in the research that gastric and duodenal ulcers, classic psychosomatic disorders, did not occur in spite of the anxiety and tension of life in the Ghetto. The reason for their non-appearence was disclosed by the studies on gastric acidity: hyperacidity was never found; instead, very low values of both free and combined acid were encountered, sometimes to the point of total achylia.[10]

Bile was very thin and was poorly excreted. Liver function tests showed a latent hepatic insufficiency. The digestive enzymes of the pancreas were found to be within normal limits.

Urine analysis was, surprisingly, normal. There was no change in the diluting or concentrating powers of the kidney. The edema was proven to be primarily extra-renal in origin even though the kidney, like all the other organs, carried on its functions at a greatly diminished rate.

Many studies were made on various metabolic processes, within the bounds of experimental capabilities under the circumstances. The basal metabolism was decreased 30 to 40 per cent below normal, far lower than in myxedema; in two cases of extreme starvation cachexia it was minus 60 per cent. The specific dynamic action of protein was lowered or totally absent. The amount of carbon dioxide excreted by the lungs was greatly reduced, a concomitant of the disturbed pulmonary ventilation.[11]

Carbohydrate metabolism was intensively studied. Capillary and venous blood sugar levels were measured; glucose tolerance curves were taken. Measurements were made of the response to adrenalin and to insulin. The speed of the utilization of carbohydrates, using the respiratory quotient as a guide, was determined.[12] Prior to these studies, no extensive research into carbohydrate metabolism during starvation had been undertaken by modern methods; studies that had been made yielded equivocal results. The Warsaw studies established the reasons for the previously observed "self-healing" of diabetes. The doctors found that the highest fasting blood-sugar level was 80 mg. per cent; the mean was 60 mg. per cent; in several cases it was as low as 24 mg. per cent, a figure never previously reported in the absence of insulin adenomas or insulin shock. In spite of the low blood sugars, clinical hypoglycemic reactions were absent; the doctors interpreted this phenomenon as an indication of the paralysis of the anti-insulin mechanisms. Sugar tolerance was increased; there was no rise in the curve after stimulation by food or adrenalin. Ingestion of sugar was followed by its extremely rapid disappearance from the blood stream, indicating its quick utilization by the starving tissues. A surprising finding, in view of the theory current at the time, was that the muscles gave up their glycogen, decomposed into sugar, into the blood. Since the liver glycogen stores had already been depleted, this indicates the mobilization of the only available peripheral reserve of glycogen, that in the muscles.

The swelling occurring during famines had been noted for a long time, but the Warsaw doctors were the first to study it by modern methods. Precise measurements were taken of water intake and output, water balance, renal and extra-renal ratios of water loss, water in the circulating blood, and water in the tissues. Mineral ash studies gave information on how water was divided between the plasma and the blood cells. Vascular wall permeability and the hydrophilic action of the subcutaneous tissues were studied by well established physiologic techniques. The doctors found: (1) a great increase in the water exchange, both intake and output going up; (2) more water was obtained from liquid foods than from that formed during the combustion process; (3) extra-renal loss of water was within normal limits, but excretion through the kidneys was increased; (4) even edematous patients excreted large amounts of water; (5) hydremia, an increased amount of water in the circulating blood, was constant in starvation; (6) the blood cells paradoxically became more desiccated and the plasma more dilute; (7) capillary permeability was unchanged; and (8) tissue hydrophilia increased, resulting in migration of fluid from the blood to the body spaces, thus bringing on edema, hydrothorax and ascites.[13]

The studies on mineral metabolism were broken off in the middle. The only detailed findings from which conclusions could be drawn were those on chlorides. Other than the expected findings, of low blood chlorides and the passage of chlorides from the plasma to the red blood cells, nothing unusual was noted.[14]

The alkalinity of the blood was studied in detail, as was the excretion of acid components in the urine, gastric juice and the expired air. The majority of cases showed a decrease in body alkalinity. Urinary ammonia excretion was increased, shown by the low titrable acidity. Many controlled experiments showed the presence of an acidosis uncompensated for by any increase in pulmonary ventilation or gastric acidity. Such an acidosis was another sign of the rigidity of the circulatory, respiratory and digestive systems. The acidosis, in turn, caused multiple disturbances in body functions.[15]

Spectrophotometric and micro-methods were used, together with other standard techniques, in the investigation of nitrogen metabolism. The results theoretically expected in a low protein, low calorie diet were obtained, plus the observation that creatine was excreted, a definitely abnormal condition.[16]

No studies on vitamin balance were made. The vitamin content of the diet was low to start with and was further lowered by the prolonged cooking of the soups dispensed by the soup kitchens and by the various processes used to preserve food. In addition, vitamin assimilation was also interfered with by the achlorhydria and by the rapid passage of food through the intestinal tract. The small amount of vitamins was balanced, however, by the very low calorie diet, the doctors said, basing their opinion on authorities who found that vitamin needs increase with the increase of calories. No clear-cut proof of any avitaminotic syndrome was found in any of the patients. There was no rickets, no scurvy, no night blindness, no keratomalacia, no pellagra. When hypo-vitaminosis-B was suspected in several cases of polyneuritis or of edema mistaken for beri-

beri and yeast given therapeutically, no improvement took place. "From our own knowledge we can state that no vitamin nor vitamin complex can eliminate the clinical or biochemical disturbances found in starvation disease."[17]

Immunologic reactions to tuberculosis were studied in great detail. The doctors were interested in finding out why starvation favors the development of tuberculosis.[18] Besides the physical and physiologic changes (pulmonary atony, poor aeration, low vital capacity, poor pulmonary circulation), a lack of immunity was also found. It was discovered that, even with gross tuberculosis, the intradermal and conjunctival tuberculin tests were negative.

The lack of response to tuberculin led to several studies on allergic reactions in general. Bronchial asthma and hives were rare, as were other diseases attributed to allergens. The skin sensitivity was diminished in all the tests made.

AUTOPSIES

There was plenty of autopsy material. From January 1, 1940, to July 22, 1942, 3658 autopsies were done. Of these, 492 were cases of "pure" starvation, proved by the absence of any complicating disease. Obviously, it was technically impossible to do an autopsy on every patient dying in the hospital, especially in starvation cases, which ran to 20 to 30 per cent of the total deaths daily. The care with which the autopsies were done is shown by the meticulously detailed charts and summaries, as well as by the protocols.[19]

Sections were taken and examined microscopically. For the first time in medical literature, the microscopic appearance of sections of the nervous system in individuals dying of starvation was reported. Careful descriptions were made of the slides taken from the endocrine glands, the heart, and all the other organs and tissues. Considering the condition under which the doctors labored, it is astonishing to read their reports about the microscopic appearance of the pituitary gland, about special stains for iron in liver cells, about minute changes in the layers of the skin.

The investigators found, as others had before them, total disappearance of all adipose tissue and an atrophy of the vital organs. The skeletal muscles were greatly shrunken. They pointed out that such changes are understandable because when the body does not get sufficient caloric material for its energy needs from food it first uses up all its own reserves and then is forced to burn its own tissues.

A surprising finding was the presence of a senile type of emphysema of the lungs, even in young people. Such changes were regarded as the result of atrophic changes in the lung tissues.

All the organs of the body (heart, liver, spleen, kidneys, etc.) showed atrophy, with one exception—the brain. Its weight, although less than normal, usually was far greater in proportion to that of the other organs.

One striking disagreement with other authorities who stressed the frequency of hemorrhage during starvation was noted: it appeared in only two of the cases studied in Warsaw (excluding the small number of minor intestinal bleedings and the greater number in pseudo-dysentery). About the latter, the doctors noted that the intestinal changes were characterized by mild inflammation superimposed on more or less swelling of the mucous membranes of the intestine. They felt that these swellings were symptomatic of the general tendency to edema found in starvation. They concluded that cases with intestinal changes resembling those in true dysentery should be regarded as having a complication of starvation disease because of the gross and microscopic evidence of their recent origin. Such changes should be considered either as the result of secondary infection on the swollen intestinal mucosa or as mucosal lesions from abnormal toxic metabolic products, such as occur in uremia; they have nothing in common with true dysentery and should be properly labeled pseudo-dysentery.

"Bone material taken in the autopsies was destroyed during the expulsion from the Ghetto."[20] Note was made, however, of the marked porosity of the bones. Fracture of the neck of the femur was frequent. The surgeons often complained of the poor quality of the bony structures, which made healing difficult and operative technique sometimes impossible. In one preparation from the head of the femur, bone porosity and decalcification were present, changes halfway between osteoporosis and osteomalacia. The doctors concluded from their studies that it is likely that hunger osteopathy is not a distinct anatomico-clinical entity, but rather that, under this name, different bony changes with a common etiology have been described, occurring in various stages of prolonged malnutrition. The bony changes vary depending on the degree of malnutrition and other conditions, thus explaining why, under the name of hunger osteopathy, a series of changes have been reported, starting with common osteoporosis and going on to atrophies, decalcifications and osteomalacia. "Hunger osteopathy" is merely another sign of the general atrophy of the organs so typical of starvation disease.

The rarity with which amyloidosis appeared (6 cases in all), was commented on. Its incidence was to be expected in view of the prevalence of tuberculosis and chronic suppurative conditions; however, it was not found even in those cases of very long standing infection. The investigators felt that the essential cause of the rarity of amyloidosis in their material was the great lack of protein in the diet, thereby agreeing with the Japanese authorities (especially Tanaki), who explain the infrequent occurrence of amyloidosis in the Japanese by the lack of sufficient protein in the Japanese diet.

7. The Researchers

SUCH WAS THE WORK DONE IN THE GHETTO. THE MOST CASUAL reader, whether physician or layman, cannot help but be struck by the recurring phrases in their papers that betoken the life of the researchers. "Unfortunately our work was interrupted"—by the mass round-up and deportation to the gas chambers at Treblinka. "This work has disappeared"—leafed through by the German looters of the vacant apartments, thrown on the blood-stained floor, and finally burned to ashes with the rest of the Ghetto. "We could not pursue this phase of the investigation for technical reasons"—because every reagent that was used, every X-ray film, meant that much less food for the investigators and the food they had was little enough. "We gave the patient 120 ml. of blood"—not more, because the blood they gave was their own. "We procured apparatus"—from the smugglers. "This work was unfinished for reasons not of our own choosing"—but by choice of the German overlords.

To let perish the memory of the noble men and women

who participated in the research and who are now dead would be wrong, just as wrong as not to honor those still alive.

Dr. Roza Amzel (1906–1943)

After having received her degree in microbiology early in the 1930's, she worked in several State institutions until she became associated in 1937 with Dr. Ludwik Hirszfeld, who regarded her as his "trusty right hand."[1] Together they helped to develop bacteriologic research in Poland. She was extremely talented, enthusiastic and sincere, always ready to try out new ideas and with the faculty of generating desire for research in others.

For a time she taught at the Pasteur Institute in Paris and then returned to Poland for an investigation into the treatment of typhoid fever and later joined with Dr. Hirszfeld in an extensive study on blood groups. In 1939, she was again at the Pasteur Institute. She came back to Poland at the first rumblings of war. During the bombing of Warsaw, she helped in the organization of a blood transfusion service for which she received much praise.

Devoted to her work, she wanted to stay in the Ghetto to do what she could for her suffering compatriots. The "resettlement" of July 1942 made her fearful for the life of her old mother with whom she lived. They made several attempts to escape together from the Ghetto and finally succeeded. They hid on the "Aryan" side for almost a year, in various places begrudgingly given by former colleagues and friends, having to change their hide-outs frequently because of fear that their hosts' neighbors would discover them. They were forced to spend large amounts of money on bribes and rent charges. Almost at the end of their tether towards the latter part of 1943, they were finally denounced by the *concierge* of the building where they were staying, turned over to the SS, and shot.[2]

Dr. Emil Apfelbaum (1890–1946)

Dr. Apfelbaum received his M.D. degree from the University of Warsaw in 1922. He had an extensive practice as a cardiologist in that city as well as being engaged in research into diseases of the circulation at the University Clinic in Internal Medicine.

He succeeded in obtaining false identification papers and escaped from the Ghetto at the end of January 1943. He remained in hiding on the "Aryan" side until the liberation. After the war, he changed his name to Kowalski because, he said, "he hated the Germans so much he could no longer bear a German name."

He died suddenly, presumably of a heart attack, on the street in Warsaw, on January 12, 1946.

Dr. Zdzislaw Askanas (1910–   )

He received his M.D. degree from the University of Warsaw in 1935. In March 1943, he left the Ghetto and remained in hiding from the Gestapo until the abortive Warsaw uprising of 1944 in which he took an active part and during which he organized a field hospital for the civilian population evacuated from the city. After the liberation he served in the Polish Army. Demobilized in 1946, he took a position in the Internal Medicine Division of the Ministry of Health. In 1950 he became Docent and in 1954 Professor in the Medical Faculty of the University of Warsaw. At present, Dr. Askanas is Chief of the Fourth Clinic in Internal Medicine and Consultant in Cardiology at Warsaw University.

Dr. Owsiej Bielenki (1884–1943)

Dr. Bielenki took his degree in science in a Russian university and the M.D. degree in Warsaw in 1913, under the

Tsarist regime. His reputation as a specialist in diseases of the lung spread all over Poland. His practice was large, not only because of his knowlege, but also because of the personal magnetism which made his patients adore him. He was tall and thin, with an appearance that inspired confidence and with a gentle smile that convinced his patients of his interest in them.[3]

In the spring of 1940, before the closing of the Ghetto, he became Chief of the Division of Internal Medicine and Infectious Diseases at the Czysta Hospital and retained that position after the removal of the hospital inside the Ghetto walls.[4]

After the hospital broke up, he got a "right to live" card as a factory worker. He worked in the factory up until the liquidation of the Ghetto on April 18, 1943.[5] On that day, together with the other workers in his shop, he was sent to the Trawniki Labor Camp. There he helped in the organization of a camp hospital for the benefit of his fellow prisoners. He was killed in the mass extermination of the camp in November 1943.[6]

Dr. Leon Blacher (1894–1942)

An M.D. since 1922, Dr. Blacher practiced in Warsaw. He took an active interest in the research project and was assigned to write the section on the coagulation of the blood in starvation. His work was lost when he was taken away to Treblinka in the July 1942 "action."

Dr. Anna Braude-Heller (1888–1943)

Dr. Anna Braude-Heller, the daughter of a wealthy family, studied in Switzerland, taking her medical degree at Zurich in 1911. While there, she naturally mingled with her compatriots, most of them emigrated Bundists. From them she learned Socialist ideas and ideals and through them she met her future husband, Heller, an engineer. She returned to Poland in 1914 to start what was to become her life-work—the care of poor children. One of her first accomplishments was the organization of a home for abandoned or war-orphaned children. After the war was over, she was a moving spirit in the development of the Medem Sanitarium and took the post of chief medical advisor.[7] She later became the medical director of the Bauman-Berson Children's Hospital on Sliska Street, an institution whose fame was widespread under her administration. During the siege of Warsaw in World War II, under her guidance the hospital became a center for first aid and care of the wounded.[8]

With the establishment of the Ghetto, the Children's Hospital took on ever-increasing importance. Dr. Braude-Heller carried on despite the most heart-breaking obstacles, not the least of which was the depletion of the staff from hunger, typhus and "resettlement." After each setback she started over again to make the hospital a functioning place for the healing of sick children. To repeated offers of help in escaping from the Ghetto, she replied, "I am not going. I have agreed to send out my son with his wife and child. As long as there are Jews in the Ghetto I am needed here and here will I stay."

The total destruction of the hospital did not stop her. She worked as a doctor for the Resistance fighters. Her end came on May 3, 1943. She was killed in a bunker under the courtyard of the defunct hospital on Gensia Street, at her post to the last.[9]

Dr. Chaim Einhorn (1910–   )

He received his medical degree in 1935 from the University of Nancy. Certified to practice in Warsaw in 1937, he worked as an assistant in the Holy Ghost Clinic under

Professor Filinski until 1939 when all the Jews were forced out of the hospital. He then became an assistant in the Czysta Hospital in the service of Dr. Beiles. After the latter was arrested in 1941 for crossing to the "Aryan" side, Dr. Einhorn took his place as head of the Division of Internal Medicine in the quarters at 2 Leszno Street. At the same time he worked at the tuberculosis preventorium center for refugees at Grzybowska Street, where Dr. Bielenki was director. He was also a doctor at the refugee center at 19 Niska Street, from which cases were chosen for referral for study on the hunger project.

Dr. Einhorn managed to escape to the "Aryan" side during the January 1943 uprising by bribing one of the wall guards. He remained hidden in a cellar until the liberation. He left Poland in 1946, going to Austria, where he was placed in charge of a displaced persons hospital (for lung diseases) in Hallein. There he remained until 1948. He now practices as an internist with special interest in pulmonary disorders in Tel Aviv, Israel.

Dr. Regina Elbinger (1889–1943)

Dr. Elbinger's certification to practice in Poland was delayed for two years because she received her medical degree from a foreign university. It was not until 1937 that she started her career as a pediatrician at the Bauman-Berson Hospital. At the outbreak of the first epidemic she was appointed head of the Typhus Fever Division in the hospital. She perished during the Ghetto uprising of April 1943.

Dr. Simon Fajgenblat (1900–1944)

Dr. Fajgenblat (M.D., University of Warsaw, 1930) was a well-known ophthalmologist in Warsaw. Shortly after the 1942 liquidations, he and his wife, Janina, also an ophthalmologist, escaped from the Ghetto and remained in hiding until the 1944 uprising, in which he took part. Severely wounded, he was taken to a secret hospital where he died. During the chaotic time of the revolt, he had become separated from his wife. After the liberation, in 1945, she finally discovered what had happened to him. Overwhelmed by the news, she committed suicide.

Dr. Henryk Fenigstein (1913–   )

Dr. Fenigstein attended the University of Warsaw until 1937 and then the Medical Officers' School in Warsaw until 1938, when he received his medical degree. In 1939, on service with the Polish Army, he was wounded and taken prisoner. He was released from a prisoner-of-war camp in April 1940, and allowed to return to Warsaw. From May 1940 until the end of the Ghetto he was associated with the Czysta Hospital as an assistant in the Department of Pathology. During that time he did close to three thousand autopsies and, besides participating in the research on hunger, wrote a number of medical papers, all of which were lost.

Captured by the Nazis in April 1943 during the burning of the Ghetto, he was sent first to the concentration camp at Lublin, and then to the camp at Budzyn. There he was kept until May 23, 1944, when he was successively transferred to the camps at Radom, Auschwitz, Vaihingen, Hessenthal, and finally, Dachau. Liberated by the American Army on April 30, 1945, he started to work immediately as a doctor in the UNRRA Hospital in Munich. He left this post in August 1948 to become an assistant in the obstetrics and gynecology department of the Munich University Polyclinic. Since the end of 1948, he has been practicing in Toronto, Canada.[10]

Fajga Ferszt (1917–1942)

Miss Ferszt was a microbiologist, a graduate of a Polish school. She was an assistant to Dr. Goliborska in the Children's Hospital. In July 1942, she was ordered by the Germans to report to a labor camp to work as a nurse there. She never returned to the Ghetto and presumably died in the camp.[11]

Dr. Julian Fliederbaum (1898–1943)

Soon after he had received his M.D. degree in 1924 from the University of Petrograd, Dr. Fliederbaum became a successful internist in Vilna, Lithuania. Before the outbreak of World War II, he had become Chief of the Endocrinology Service at the Vilna Cancer Hospital. Like so many refugees at the beginning of the war, he and his family fled to the presumed safety of Warsaw. There he joined his heavily laden colleagues in their desperate task of trying to hold back the advancing mortality in the Ghetto.

After the isolation hospital on Stawki Street was changed to a general hospital, he became its director and, as such, encouraged and took part in the research project.[12]

In the final liquidation of the Ghetto, rather than submit to a further tortured life under German rule, he, together with his wife and little son, jumped from the fourth floor of their apartment building and were killed instantly.[13]

Dr. Theodosia Goliborska (1899–)

Dr. Goliborska received her medical degree from the University of Warsaw in 1926. She became head of the Department of Pathology at the Bauman-Berson Hospital

and remained in that position until she finally left the
Ghetto in 1942 after the "resettlement." With the aid of
friends from the "Aryan" side, she escaped by bribing the
wall guards. She stayed in hiding on the "Aryan" side until
the liberation. In 1946 she emigrated to Australia, where
she is now practicing.

Dr. Ari (Leo) Heller (1917–   )

Dr. Heller, the son of Dr. Anna Braude-Heller, succeeded in escaping with his wife and child from the Ghetto
during the January 1943 "action." They remained in hiding on the "Aryan" side until the liberation. He took his
M.B. degree in 1945 at Lublin. For a short time he was
an assistant in the biochemistry department of the University of Lublin, and then went to the University of Breslau.
In April 1946 he moved to Sweden where he worked as a
biochemist, and, since 1948, as a virologist. He is now associate professor at the National Bacteriologic Laboratory in
Stockholm.

Jerzy Herzenkruk (1919–1943)

Mr. Herzenkruk had studied dentistry for four years before the beginning of World War II and it was only the
collapse of Poland and its educational institutions that
prevented him from getting his degree. His previous training and his enthusiasm were a great help in some of the
more tedious aspects of the research project. In September
of 1942, after the "Big Kettle," he and his wife managed
to make their way to the "Aryan" side. There they were
in hiding until they were discovered and denounced by
blackmailers and killed early in 1943.

Dr. Mieczyslaw Kocen (1896–1943)

Dr. Kocen got his medical degree at the University of
Rostov, in Russia, in 1920. Certified by the University of

Warsaw in 1935, he returned to Lodz, his native city, where he became a clinical pathologist, with particular interest in the field of hematology. He became director of the Department of Pathology at the Poznanski Hospital in that city. He was also in charge of a similar department in the Polish government institution "Kasa Chorych," besides having a large private practice. In 1939, when the Germans incorporated Lodz into the Reich, he and his family were deported to Krakow, and thence to Warsaw in 1940. In July 1942, after the mass deportations had begun, he found a way to send his ten-year-old son (now a physician in England) to the "Aryan" side. In October 1942, his wife was killed. He himself was taken to Treblinka for extermination after the liquidation of the hospital in January 1943.

Dr. Israel Milejkowski (1887–1943)

Dr. Milejkowski received his M.D. degree from Warsaw University in 1914 and practiced there as a dermatologist and venereologist. In addition to his medical work, he was an active leader in the General Zionist Party. One day, soon after the capture of Warsaw, he was set upon by a gang of Germans on the street. Disregarding his Red Cross band, they proceeded to beat him up, and then bade him sing and dance. He said later of this episode, "I could have shown character and refused, in which case the Nazis would have killed me. That would not have been too pleasant for me—so I danced."[14] Because of his prominence as a physician and as a Zionist he was appointed by the German authorities as one of the original members of the Judenrat.[15]

He used his position to organize a Public Health Service for the Ghetto in order to mitigate the physical evils of the occupation as much as possible. On the spiritual side he

continued his efforts to maintain the sense of Jewish soli-
darity in his brethren, heavily borne down by their daily
trials and tribulations.

Together with other leaders in the cultural life of the
Ghetto, he organized discussion groups[16] and actively
participated in the setting up of the illegal courses for
medical students, one of which, the course on general
pathology, he gave himself.[17]

His attitude to life in the Ghetto was clear: he regarded
it not as a throwback to the Middle Ages, as did so many of
his contemporaries, but rather as a new, a degenerative,
development in Jewish history in which no cultural life
could evolve as it had in the medieval Ghettos. He felt that
the Jews had to bend under the blows of the oppressors, to
shrink away, in order that they might survive; he felt that
the defeat of the Nazis was certain and, meanwhile, as
much of Jewish culture as possible should be preserved. He
looked on the research into hunger as one aspect of Jewish
survival. In his reply to a questionaire from the Oneg
Shabbat (the legal pseudonym for the Underground Ar-
chives), in one section he said, "We will later—after the
catastrophe—be able to demonstrate to the world that the
murderous enemy could not destroy us. In the very moment while we are sitting here there is going on a small
scientific session, concerning the Ghetto. The result of this
work will be published later and I hope that it will be of
great interest to the whole world."[18]

Dr. Milejkowski happened to be in the building where
the *Judenrat* had its offices on the day that the Germans
told the chairman, Czerniakow, that ten thousand Jews
were to be supplied daily for "resettlement" in the East.
Unable to bring himself to comply with the order to ar-
range for the deportations, Czerniakow committed suicide

by taking potassium cyanide. Dr. Milejkowski, summoned when the body was found, could do nothing other than pronounce him dead.

The terrible scenes of the deportations and the later discovery that "resettlement" really meant gassing and incineration made Dr. Milejkowske change his opinion about how the Jews should act toward the Germans. He gave up the idea of passive resistance and was taking steps to join the Jewish Fighting Organization. His resolution came too late, however. On January 18, 1943, the Germans started a new liquidation. On January 19, all the *Judenrat* officials were arrested, including Dr. Milejkowski. True to his new idea, he did not go quietly to the *Umschlagsplatz*, but had to be dragged there by force. His last words as he was loaded into the freight car for Treblinka were, "Murderers! Our blood will fall on your heads!"[19]

Dr. Ryszard Pakswer (1912–1943?)

Other than the dates of his birth and the granting of a medical degree to him by the University of Krakow in 1936, nothing is in the available records about Dr. Pakswer. It is hinted that he was one of the doctors taken away in January 1943, to Treblinka.

Dr. Moryc (Moritz) Plonskier (1896–1942)

Dr. Plonskier took his medical training at the University of Warsaw, getting his degree from there in 1925. Until 1939 he was head of the Department of Pathologic Anatomy at the Czysta Hospital. In that year he left for Lwow to take up a position there. He returned to Warsaw in 1940 and became a staff member at the Bauman-Berson Children's Hospital. He was taken away in the July 1942 deportations.

Dr. Boleslaw Raszkes (1902–1942)

Dr. Raszkes, a 1928 graduate of the University of Warsaw, practiced as a dermatologist in that city. He was an
assistant in the Dermatology Clinic of his alma mater. He
was killed at Treblinka in July 1942.

Dr. Israel Rotbalsam (Rom) (1909–   )

Dr. Rotbalsam got his M.D. at the University of Warsaw
in 1932. From 1933 to 1935 he was on the staff of the Holy
Ghost Hospital; from 1935 to 1938, with the Pediatric
Clinic of Warsaw University; and from 1938, on the staff
of the Bauman-Berson Children's Hospital. He remained
and worked in the Ghetto until after the January 1943
attack, when he succeeded in making his way to the
"Aryan" side. The Gestapo was hot on his trail, however,
and he was forced to return to the relative safety of the
Ghetto in March of 1943. On May 11, 1943, during the
uprising in the Ghetto, he was captured by the S.S. and
sent to Treblinka and from there to the concentration
camp at Majdanek. The next two years were spent in various concentration camps, including Buchenwald and Mau-
thausen. He was liberated from the last by the advancing
American Army. After making his way to Paris, where he
stayed for seven months, he left for Palestine. He began to
work (and still does so) as a pediatrician for Kupat Holim
(the Workers' Sickness Fund) except for one year's mili-
tary service during Israel's war for independence in 1948.
He now resides in Tel Aviv, Israel.

Dr. Joseph Stein (1904–1943)

Dr. Stein, described by those who knew him as a sweet
and gentle man, had an unusually broad education, being
a Doctor of Philosophy as well as having the M.D. degree

granted by the University of Warsaw in 1927. Before the war, as an anatomist and pathologist of great reputation, he was given a grant by the Potocki Foundation to do research in cancer as an associate in the Department of Pathology at the Holy Ghost Hospital.[20]

In spite of the fact that he had been baptized into the Catholic faith and that he regarded himself as completely Polish, he was forced into the Ghetto.[21] His extensive collection of typhus fever specimens was broken up by the Germans and distributed to various pathology institutes in Germany. He refused all offers of help to escape from the Ghetto, saying that, as Director of the Czysta Hospital, his duty was to his patients and he had to stay with them. In the last days of the Ghetto, on May 6, 1943, he was taken with his wife and daughter to Treblinka, where they were all killed.[22]

Dr. Mieczyslaw Szejnman (1901–1943)

A graduate of Warsaw University in 1928, Dr. Szejnman confined his practice to internal medicine, with particular interest in hematology. During the early period of the Ghetto he was very active in the anti-typhus fever inoculation campaign.[23] He managed to leave the Ghetto just before the April 1943, uprising, but was caught by the Gestapo on the "Aryan" side and was killed.

Dr. Michael Szajnman (1912–1942)

A pediatrician since 1936 (M.D., University of Warsaw), Dr. Szajnman took an active part in the research on hunger. He himself died of malnutrition early in 1942.

Dr. Suzanne Szejnfinkiel

Other than the fact that she received her degree in biology, no information is available.

Dr. Ichaskil Wohl (1895–1943)

He received his medical degree in 1923 from the University of Vienna and was licensed to practice in Poland in 1926. Influenced by his brother-in-law, the noted Mizrachi leader, Dr. Wolfsberg, he took a leading part in many Jewish community activities. He was indefatigable inside the Ghetto, working for his co-religionists, feeling certain that the Jews would outlive Hitler as they had Haman.[24] It was only after the great deportations of July 1942 that he realized that survival was possible only outside of the Ghetto walls. He cast about for ways to save his only daughter, but was unsuccessful. The Polish nuns who took so many other Jewish children into their convents, saying they were Polish orphans, refused to take her because she did not have a "good visage;" with her black hair and dark eyes she "looked Jewish."[25]

In February 1943, he, with his wife and daughter, finally escaped to the "Aryan" side. There they lived for several months, kept by friendly Poles, until the end so common to other escapees overtook them also. They were discovered by *schmaltzovniks* (blackmailers) and, when their money gave out, were turned over to the Germans, who killed all three.

Jeanne (Janina) Zarchi (?–1942)

Miss Zarchi was the daughter of a popular general practitioner in Zambrow, which place she left to study medicine in Warsaw. She disappeared in September 1942, presumably taken in the "Big Kettle" of that month.

Dr. Kazimierz Zweibaum (Zakrzewski) (1918–   )

Dr. Zakrzewski, the son of Professor Julius Zweibaum, took his medical training and got his degree from the University of Lwow in 1941. When the Germans invaded the U.S.S.R., he went to Warsaw, where his parents still were. He took an active part in the research project. He survived the German occupation and continued his medical studies after the war. He became a Docent in 1954 and now is Professor at a Warsaw Research Institute.

8. Evaluation

INTRODUCTION

The work was done. The question arises—has it any value for medical science? Perhaps the unhappy doctors in the Ghetto, prey to the same intellectual deterioration they so vividly described as a result of starvation, themselves were deluded into thinking that they were accomplishing a meritorious piece of work. Perhaps they were merely occupying themselves, in an existentialist sense, because they were unwilling to face the facts of life—and death. Perhaps the material (fateful word!), was insufficient in quantity or poorly chosen. Perhaps the details of the experiments were faultily thought out or their execution mishandled. Perhaps the conclusions were already drawn before the project was started.

True enough, such delusions have appeared before, and with less reason, in the history of science. The great Newton occupied himself with apocalyptic calculations. The Ptolemaic theory was well-founded on careful observation. The early scientists found no difficulty in proving experimentally the existence of phlogiston and the caloric fluid.

There is only one adequate test for the value of a scientific study such as this and that is the judgment of other investigators in the same field. To determine whether the Warsaw Ghetto project on starvation was a worth-while effort the specialists in the field of nutrition must be consulted. And to do that, pertinent questions must be asked: Was this study necessary? Has not this work been done before? What did the material consist of? What were the controls? How well qualified were the investigators? Were the results explicable? Were the conclusions valid? Is there evidence from other sources to support the conclusions? And finally, what was added to the fund of scientific knowledge?

NECESSITY FOR THE PROJECT

There can be no question as to the necessity for the study. Probably the most comprehensive review of the literature on famine and starvation is found in the Minnesota Experiment Report by Professor Keys and his associates. After going over the literature they came to the conclusion, before starting their own experiment during World War II, that up to that time there had been no really thorough scientific study of the effects of chronic under-nutrition, of starvation, in human beings. All studies done before then were incomplete, lacking in essential data, measurements, etc., and consisted mainly of clinical observations.[1] Their conclusion was accepted by the United States government and by the various foundations and organizations that supported their extensive and expensive study. As will be shown, other than the Minnesota study, there has been no other research comparable to the Warsaw project.

That other authorities felt the need for such studies can be seen from the following list of similar researches carried out from the beginning of World War II:

(a) the Belgian studies of 1940–1944, done with good technical facilities and access to medical libraries and not disturbed by any breakdown in civil order, but very limited by the small number of cases observed;

(b) the Louvain Prison studies, where four hundred men received 1700-1800 calories per day;

(c) the siege of Leningrad reports, which gave little factual data in detail on the previous degree of nutrition or on the effects of starvation on the population as a whole;

(d) the Paris mental hospital reports from 1941–1942, giving incomplete data on patients living on 1500-1800 calories per day for about twenty months;

(e) the Danish reports on concentration camp prisoners, compiled after the liberation, on a total of 1282 persons.[2]

It is obvious that the Warsaw project was not an idle gesture but a definite attempt on the part of the Ghetto doctors to fill a gap in scientific knowledge.

MATERIAL AND TECHNIQUES

But regardless of the doctors' good intentions, the project, in order to qualify as a serious investigation, has to meet definite standards as to the type of material studied. On the basis of extensive study of data from various sources, Keys and his associates came to the conclusion that

starvation could be studied only if the subjects had sub-
sisted for from six to twelve months on 30 to 50 per cent
fewer calories than previously consumed, leading to a loss
in body weight of from 20 to 40 per cent.[3] In their own
study of thirty-six conscientious objectors, they therefore
set up a diet of from 1570 to 1700 calories for the starvation period of 24 weeks, giving an average weight loss of 25
per cent; the average daily diet consisted of 275 gms. carbohydrates, 50 gms. protein and 30 gms. fats.[4] For comparison with previous studies the following table is in-
structive:[5]

Group		Average Daily Calorie Intake
French Prisoners of War (World War I)		2245
Germans—Blockade Period,	April 1916	2343
	July 1916	2232
	April 1917	1985
German Prisoner of War Camp (World War II)		1611
Paris Mental Hospital	April 1941	1447
Netherlands Famine—Third quarter of 1944		1529
Dachau	September 1944	1017
	May 1945	533

Needless to say, the Warsaw Ghetto supplied patients in
sufficient quantity and sufficiently starved to meet the cri-
teria. In discussing the Warsaw report, which was made
available to him only after the Minnesota Experiment was
completed, Keys comments:

The majority of detailed scientific reports on the effects of
famine in man have been based on observations made during
the phase of refeeding or attempted rehabilitation. Though a
few days or weeks of medical care and extra alimentation
may not greatly alter the picture, the situation in the actual
period of starvation is of particular interest. The studies made
in the Warsaw Ghetto are of unusual value. Technical work
at Warsaw was surprisingly sound (in spite of the conditions
under which they worked) and has the great advantage that

it concerns a population group of all ages and both sexes. . . .
[Autopsies were important] but more important were the
tests and measurements made in the living.[6]

As for the autopsies in starved patients, there had never
been so many nor so detailed post-mortem examinations
giving weights of the organs as were done in the Ghetto.[7]
The Danish investigators say,

A remarkable contribution to our present knowledge of
famine disease has been made by Jewish physicians in the
ruins of the besieged Ghetto of Warsaw. In spite of the ap-
palling circumstances the authors have succeeded in perform-
ing an excellent clinical, physiological and anatomical study
. . . on the active phase of starvation . . . thanks to surprisingly
sound technical investigations, this monograph can be considered as unique.[8]

Controls present no problem. The meticulous care with
which all except "pure" cases were excluded, the verifica-
tions at autopsy, the comparison with previously studied
subjects (as in Dr. Apfelbaum's work on heart dysfunction)—all these were controls. An even better control on
the results is available by checking those obtained in Warsaw with those in other studies on semi-starved patients.

COMPARATIVE FINDINGS

The most cursory comparison of the results from various
studies shows how careful, even under the most distressing
conditions, were the Ghetto doctors. Any detailed analysis
would be out of place here, but some brief mention must
be made of the findings elsewhere and how they agree or
disagree with the findings in Warsaw.

The Minnesota group found the same blood changes as
were found in Warsaw and the same block in migration of
cells from the bone marrow into the circulating blood.

This lack of "ejectory stimulus" and the lack of parallelism in the red and white cell counts was also noted by Gillman and Gillman in their studies of chronically undernourished black South Africans.[9]

The latter authors confirm the rarity of peptic ulcer in semi-starved individuals,[10] as do the Danes.[11]

As for blood volume, so carefully studied in Warsaw, Keys reports a relative increase of plasma volume in starvation along with an absolute decrease of 8.6 per cent in total blood volume, findings consistent with those in Warsaw. The hydration of the tissues and its apparent lack of relation to osmotic pressure has been noted by many other authors. The peculiarity of the edema has been confirmed by a Mexican group.[12]

The cold cyanotic skin and the pigmentary changes were found in South Africans, Americans, and Mexicans, as well as in the Warsaw Jews. The apathy and depression occurring in chronic hunger have been a constant finding in all the studies along with the unchanged sensory perception and the lessened reactivity to drugs and antigens. The low basal metabolic rate, so crucial for an understanding of the whole syndrome, is confirmed by the Minnesota and Mexican data.[13]

The methods of the Warsaw doctors gave almost the same result (about -50%) for cardiac minute-volume as the elaborate technique used in Minnesota (-44.8%).[14] Low voltage of the ECG, bradycardia and disturbances in carbohydrate metabolism were found both in Warsaw and in Minnesota.[15] In agreement also was the striking absence of the classic vitamin deficiencies such as keratomalacia and scurvy.[16] As for rickets, Wilder, in his foreword to Keys' book, comments on how rarely rickets is found in the chronically calorie-deficient child.[17] Even such a comparatively trivial observation that the parotid glands become enlarged was not overlooked, a finding previously noted and forgotten.[18]

Were there any differences at all? Indeed there were. Emphysema, so prominent in the Warsaw report, was not found at all in the Minnesota experiment.[19] Gingivitis was found in both studies, but dental caries only in Warsaw.[20] And yet, both of these signs, by their very nature taking a long time to develop, may have been absent in Minnesota because of the shorter (24 weeks) duration of the experiment.

One other difference, non-medical, existed. Keys remarks on the great increase in crimes of violence during periods of famine.[21] In the Warsaw Ghetto, all the violence came from the starvers, not the starved.

CONCLUSIONS

On the basis of their findings the Warsaw doctors came to the conclusion that prolonged starvation in human beings leads to a specific disease entity which they called "starvation disease." They regarded this disease as one of adaptation to a peculiar prolonged and ungovernable stress—calorie deficiency. The same inference was reached by other workers unaware of the Ghetto studies. Professor Kleiber says, "An animal dying of starvation may be compared to the engine an automobile has which is left idling at a very low rate and which 'dies' when the rate of idling is too low to maintain the proper function of the carburetor and of the sparking device."[22] Keys and his collaborators agree:

Adaptation [is] a useful adjustment to altered circumstances. When the total basal metabolic rate decreases in starvation . . . it is certainly a favorable change in that it reduces the caloric deficit as compared with what it would be in the absence of such change in the basal metabolism. To the starving individual the reduced metabolic rate means that, at a given food intake, this rate of loss of strength and endurance is diminished and that, to cover it to the limit, he will survive longer.[23]

They point out that a decrease of 40 per cent in the BMR is equivalent to a gain of almost six hundred calories per day.

The best example of the adaptive process is seen in the circulatory system. Keys says, as did the Ghetto investigators, ". . . the slow heart rate is adaptive in that it responds to a circulatory demand which is decreased because of the reduced metabolism of the body . . . the peripheral circulation is a compromise between the demands of tissue metabolism and heat conservation."[24]

The manner by which adaptation occurs is still obscure. Gillman and Gillman imply that the endocrines play a large role in the deranged metabolism of chronic undernutrition.[25] The Mexican investigators state that the syndrome is one of chronic hypopanpituitarism with secondary changes although they admit that the cause of the pituitary suppression is not known.[26] Keys and the Warsaw group also agree that hormonal changes are of great importance in the development of the syndrome.

It would be fruitless to pursue the discussion of the value of the Warsaw studies further. It is indeed a grave and wonderful thing that was done in the dark days of the Warsaw Ghetto. The fact that science has benefited by the devotion of the doctors adds further lustre to their memory.

Afterword

NO MORE FITTING TRIBUTE TO THE WARSAW RESEARCHERS can be given than that by Dr. Milejkowski, written in October, 1942:

And you, Jewish physicians, you deserve some words of recognition.

What can I say to you, my companions in misfortune, my dear colleagues? You, too, were part of the whole. You, too, were menaced by forced labor, starvation, deportation, by all the forms of death that stalked our Ghetto. And you—you gave the murderers a bold answer with your work—*"Non omnis moriar!"*

Notes

ABBREVIATIONS

BB—*The Black Book: The Nazi Crime against the Jewish People*, New York, 1946.

BBPJ—*The Black Book of Polish Jewry*, Jacob Apenszlak (ed.), New York, 1943.

BFG—*Bleter far Geshichte*, Warsaw publication of the Historical Institute in Poland.

DY—Shpizman, Leib: *Di Yidn in Nazi-Poilen*, New York, 1942.

MF—*Maladie de Famine;* Warsaw, 1946.

INTRODUCTION

1. Mitscherlich, Alexander and Mielke, Fred, *Doctors of Infamy: The Story of the Nazi Medical Crimes* (New York, 1949), p. 66.

CHAPTER 1

1. Stroop, Jürgen, *Report on the Uprising in the Jewish Residential District and its Liquidation* (Warsaw, 1958), p. 18.
2. Shoshkes, Henry, *No Traveler Returns* (New York, 1945), p. 28.
3. Sloan, Jacob (ed.), *Notes from the Warsaw Ghetto: The Journal of Emanuel Ringelblum* (New York, 1958), pp. 348-359.
4. Stroop, *op. cit.*, p. 102.
5. *Ibid.*, p. 116.

6. Hilberg, Raul, *The Destruction of the European Jews* (Chicago, 1961), p. 121.
7. Sloan, *op. cit.*, p. 97ff.
8. *Im Feuer Vergangen: Tagebücher aus dem Ghetto* (Berlin, 1959), p. 381.
9. Nirenstein, Albert, *A Tower from the Enemy* (New York, 1959), p. 4.
10. Friedman, Philip (ed.), *Martyrs and Fighters: The Epic of the Warsaw Ghetto* (New York, 1954), p. 112.

CHAPTER 2

1. DY, p. 230.
2. BBPJ, p. 180.
3. "Economic Sector of Jewish Residential District in Warsaw, Order of April 19, 1941," BFG, xii (1959), p. 65.
4. Shoshkes, *op. cit.*, p. 31.
5. DY, p. 281.
6. BBPJ, p. 173.
7. Hirszfeld, Ludwik, *Historia Jednego Życia* (Warsaw, 1957), p. 232.
8. DY, p. 242.
9. Trunk, Isaiah, "Epidemics and Mortality in the Warsaw Ghetto, 1939-1942," YIVO *Annual of Jewish Social Science* (New York, 1953), vol. 8, 94.
10. Babitz, Benjamin, "Notes from the Ghetto, Prison, and Fields," BFG, x (1957), p. 155.
11. DY, p. 234.
12. DY, p. 237.
13. Trunk, *op. cit.*, p. 95.
14. BBPJ, p. 43.
15. BBPJ, p. 221.
16. Berg, Mary, *Warsaw Ghetto: A Diary* (New York, 1945), p. 53.
17. *Ibid.*, p. 59.
18. *Ibid.*, p. 60.
19. DY, p. 272.
20. Berg, *op. cit.*, p. 86, p. 88.
21. Goldstein, Bernard, *The Stars Bear Witness* (New York, 1949), p. 90.
22. BBPJ, p. 227.
23. Nirenstein, *op. cit.*, p. 5.
24. Berg, *op. cit.*, p. 90.
25. BBPJ, p. 25.
26. "Likwidacja Żydowskiej Warszawy," *Biuletyn Żydowskiego Historycznego* (Warsaw, 1951), #1, 116.
27. Hirszfeld, *op. cit.*, p. 232.
28. *Ibid.*, p. 301.
29. Ringelblum, Emanuel, "Fun di Letzten Notizen," BFG, xi (1958), 20.

30. Trunk, *op. cit.*, p. 121.
31. BB, p. 225.
32. BBPJ, pp. 44, 51.
33. *Im Feuer* . . . , p. 402.
34. Friedman, *op. cit.*, p. 61.
35. Sloan, *op. cit.*, p. 53.
36. Turkow, Jonas, *Azoy iz es Geven* (Buenos Aires, 1948), p. 123.
37. *Im Feuer* . . . , p. 372.
38. Friedman, *op. cit.*, p. 90.
39. Mazor, Michel, *La Cité Engloutie* (Paris, 1955), p. 120.
40. Turkow, *op. cit.*, p. 116.
41. *Im Feuer* . . . , p. 374.
42. Turkow, *op. cit.*, p. 125.
43. Berg, *op. cit.*, p. 32.
44. Trunk, *op. cit.*, p. 95.
45. Mazor, *op. cit.*, p. 66.
46. Sloan, *op. cit.*, p. 125.
47. Turkow, *op. cit.*, p. 124.
48. *Gazeta Żydowska*, #125, Dec. 17, 1941; order of Dr. Lauxmann, Postmaster-General of the Government-General.
49. Sloan, *op. cit.*, pp. 140, 214.
50. *Ibid.*, p. 187.
51. Berg, *op. cit.*, p. 61.

CHAPTER 3

1. Goldstein, *op. cit.*, p. 75.
2. *Ibid.*, p. 76.
3. Berg, *op. cit.*, p. 40.
4. Sloan, *op. cit.*, p. 111.
5. Bernshtein, T., "Vegn di Hitleristishe Metoden fun der Ekonomishe Eksploitatsie fun Varshever Ghetto," BFG xii (1959), p. 58.
6. Turkow, *op. cit.*, p. 128.
7. Goldstein, *op. cit.*, p. 78.
8. Hirszfeld, *op. cit.*, p. 240.
9. Sloan, *op. cit.*, p. 121.
10. Mazor, *op. cit.*, p. 154.
11. Sloan, *op. cit.*, p. 149.
12. *Ibid.*, p. 128.
13. *Ibid.*, p. 279.
14. *Im Feuer* . . . , p. 384.
15. MF, p. 11.
16. Berg, *op. cit.*, p. 72.
17. Hochberg-Marianska, Maria (ed.), *Dzieci Oskarzája* (Krakow, 1947) p. 5.
18. Hirszfeld, *op. cit.*, p. 342.
19. Turkow, *op. cit.*, p. 127.

CHAPTER 4

1. Sloan, *op. cit.*, p. 294.
2. BBPJ, p. 39.
3. Fenigstein, Henri, *Varshever Yidish Shpital besn di Nazi-Rezhim* (Frankfurt-am-Main, 1948), p. 6.
4. Hertz, J. S. (ed), *Zygelboim Buch* (New York, 1947), p. 141.
5. Sloan, *op. cit.*, p. 80.
6. Fenigstein, *op. cit.*, p. 8; Sloan, *op. cit.*, p. 113; Trunk, Isaiah, "Melchomo kegn Yidn durch Farshpreitn Krankheit," *YIVO Bleter* (New York, 1953), vol. 37, p. 113.
7. Goldstein, *op. cit.*, p. 65.
8. Reitlinger, Gerald, *The Final Solution* (London, 1953), p. 59.
9. Poliakov, Leon, *Harvest of Hate* (Syracuse, 1954), p. 92.
10. DY, p. 282.
11. Ringelblum, *op. cit.*, p. 11.
12. Trunk, "Epidemics . . . ," *op. cit.*, p. 101.
13. Friedman, *op. cit.*, p. 145.
14. BBPJ, p. 123ff.
15. Fenigstein, *op. cit.*, p. 12; Silberschein, A., *Die Juden Ausrottung in Polen* (Geneva, 1944), p. 18.
16. Seidman, Hillel, *Togbuch fun Varshever Ghetto* (Buenos Aires, 1947), p. 112; Ringelblum, *op. cit.*, p. 7.
17. Hirszfeld, *op. cit.*, p. 337.
18. Nirenstein, *op. cit.*, p. 97; Shoshkes, *op. cit.*, p. 152.
19. Fenigstein, *op. cit.*, pp. 12, 15.
20. Hirszfeld, *op. cit.*, p. 337.
21. Bielitzki, L., "Vegn der 'Aktsie' in Varshever Yidisher Shpital dem 18 January, 1943," BFG, i (1948), 211; Turkow, *op. cit.*, p. 462 Blumenthal, N., "Action," *Yad Washem Studies on the European Jewish Catastrophe and Resistance* (Jerusalem, 1960), IV, 70; *Glos Warszawy*, #6, Jan. 26, 1943.
22. Mark, Ber, *Der Oifshtand in Varshever Ghetto* (Warsaw, 1955), p. 258.
23. DY, p. 175.
24. BBPJ, p. 21.
25. DY, p. 63.
26. Sloan, *op. cit.*, p. 19.
27. *Ibid.*, p. 197.
28. Berg, *op. cit.*, p. 132.

CHAPTER 5

1. MF, p. 6.
2. MF, p. 9 ff.
3. Hirszfeld, *op. cit.*, p. 255.
4. MF, p. 17.
5. Personal communication from Dr. Witold Orlowski.

CHAPTER 6

1. MF, p. 81.
2. MF, p. 83.
3. MF, pp. 84-88.
4. MF, p. 89.
5. MF, pp. 259-264.
6. MF, p. 111.
7. MF, pp. 173-187.
8. MF, pp. 189-225.
9. MF, pp. 227-258.
10. MF, p. 107.
11. MF, p. 131.
12. MF, pp. 115-130.
13. MF, pp. 146-153.
14. MF, p. 136.
15. MF, pp. 137-144.
16. MF, pp. 145-46.
17. MF, p. 159.
18. MF, p. 91.
19. MF, pp. 33-77.
20. MF, p. 76.

CHAPTER 7

1. Hirszfeld, op. cit., p. 116.
2. Ibid., p. 396.
3. Ibid., p. 249.
4. Fenigstein, op. cit., p. 6.
5. Turkow, op. cit., p. 505.
6. Turkow, Jonas: In Kamf farn Lebn (Buenos Aires, 1949), p. 237.
7. Goldstein, op. cit., p. 156.
8. Turkow, Azoy . . . , p. 32.
9. Niger, S. (ed.), Kiddush ha-Shem (New York, 1948), p. 112.
10. Personal communication from Dr. H. Fenigstein.
11. Personal communication from Dr. T. Goliborska.
12. Hirszfeld, op. cit., p. 211.
13. Ibid., p. 373.
14. Shoshkes, op. cit., p. 55.
15. Mark, op. cit., p. 43.
16. Ringelblum, Emanual: "Fun di Letzten Notizen," BFG, xii, 1959, p. 20.
17. Hirszfeld, op. cit., p. 207.
18. "Anketen," BFG, i, 1948, pp. 189-193.
19. Mark, op. cit., p. 202.
20. Fenigstein, op. cit., p. 4.
21. Hirszfeld, op. cit., p. 340.
22. Stabholz, Tadeusz: Siedem Piekiel (Stuttgart, 1947), p. 17.

23. Hirszfeld, *op. cit.*, p. 339.
24. Seidman, *op. cit.*, p. 12.
25. Turkow, *In Kamf* . . . , p. 237.

CHAPTER 8

1. Keys, Ancel, *et al.*, *The Biology of Human Starvation* (Minneapolis, 1950), p. 19 ff.
2. Helweg-Larsen, Per, *et al.*, "Famine Disease in German Concentration Camps and Sequelae," *Acta Psychiatrica et Neurologica Scandinavica*, Supplement 83, Copenhagen, 1952.
3. Keys, *op. cit.*, p. 129.
4. *Ibid.*, p. 63.
5. *Ibid.*, p. 1239 ff.
6. *Ibid.*, p. 22.
7. *Ibid.*, p. 186.
8. Helweg-Larsen, *op. cit.*, p. 77.
9. Gillman, Joseph, and Gillman, Theodore, *Perspectives in Human Malnutrition* (New York, 1951), p. 334.
10. *Ibid.*, p. 456.
11. Helweg-Larsen, *op. cit.*, p. 282.
12. Wohl, Michael G., and Goodhart, Robert S. (eds.), *Modern Nutrition in Health and Disease* (Philadelphia, 1960), p. 875.
13. Keys, *op. cit.*, p. 317.
14. *Ibid.*, p. 616.
15. *Ibid.*, p. 562.
16. Helweg-Larsen, *op. cit.*, p. 207.
17. Keys, *op. cit.*, p. xix.
18. Hoelzel, Frederick: "Letter to the Editor," *American Journal of Clinical Nutrition*, vol. 3, Nov., 1955, 513-515.
19. Keys, *op. cit.*, p. 196.
20. *Ibid.*, p. 226.
21. *Ibid.*, p. 785.
22. Kleiber, Max, *The Fire of Life* (New York, 1961), p. 247.
23. Keys, *op. cit.*, p. 338.
24. *Ibid.*, p. 576 ff.
25. Gillman, *op. cit.*, p. 392.
26. Wohl, *op. cit.*, p. 883.

Bibliography

BOOKS

Apenszlak, Jacob (ed.). *The Black Book of Polish Jewry*. New York, 1943.

Apfelbaum, Emil (ed.). *Maladie de Famine*. Warsaw, 1946.

Berg, Mary. *Warsaw Ghetto: a Diary*. New York, 1946.

Fenigstein, Henri. *Varshever Yidish Shpital besn di Nazi-Rezhim*. Frankfurt-am-Main, 1948.

Fichez, L. F., and Klotz, A. *La Senescence Prémature et ses Traitements*. Vienna, 1961.

Friedman, Philip (ed.)."*Martyrs and Fighters: The Epic of the Warsaw Ghetto*. New York, 1954.

Gillman, Joseph, and Gillman, Theodore. *Perspectives in Human Malnutrition*. New York, 1951.

Goldstein, Bernard. *The Stars Bear Witness*. New York, 1949.

Hertz, Jacob (ed.). *Zygelboim Buch*. New York, 1947.

Hilberg, Raul. *The Destruction of the European Jews*. Chicago, 1961.

Hirszfeld, Ludwik. *Historia Jednego Życia*. Warsaw, 1957.

Hochberg-Marianska, Maria (ed.). *Dzieci Oskarzája*. Krakow, 1947.

Kermisz, Joseph (ed.). *Dokumenty i Materialy do dziejów Okupacji Niemieckiej w Polsce,* Vol. II, *"Akcje" i "Wysiedlenia."* Warsaw, 1946.

Keys, Ancel, *et al. The Biology of Human Starvation*. Minneapolis, 1950.

Kleiber, Max. *The Fire of Life*. New York, 1961.

Mark, Ber. *Der Oifshtand in Varshever Ghetto*. Warsaw, 1955.

Mazor, Michel. *La Cité Engloutie*. Paris, 1955.

Mitscherlich, Alexander, and Mielke, Fred. *Doctors of Infamy: The Story of the Nazi Medical Crimes*. New York, 1949.

Neustadt, Melech. *Hurbn un Oifshtand*. Tel Aviv, 1948.

Niger, S. (ed.). *Kiddush Ha-Shem*. New York, 1948.

Nirenstein, Albert. *A Tower from the Enemy*. New York, 1959.

Poliakov, Leon. *Harvest of Hate*. Syracuse, 1954.

Reitlinger, Gerald. *The Final Solution*. London, 1953.

Seidman, Hillel. *Togbuch fun Varshever Ghetto*. Buenos Aires, 1947.

Shoshkes, Henry. *No Traveler Returns*. New York, 1945.

Shpizman, Leib. *Di Yidn in Nazi-Poiln*. New York, 1942.

Silberschein, A. (ed.). *Die Judenausrottung in Polen*. Geneva, 1944.

Sloan, Jacob (ed.). *Notes from the Warsaw Ghetto: The Journal of Emanuel Ringelblum*. New York, 1958.

Stabholz, Tadeusz. *Siedem Piekiel*, Stuttgart, 1947.

Stempelberg, Herman (ed.). *Męczeństwo, Walka, Zagłada Żydów w Polsce*. Warsaw, 1960.

Stroop, Jürgen. *Report on the Uprising in the Jewish Residential District and its Liquidation*. Warsaw, 1958.

Szner, Zvi (ed.). *Extermination and Resistance: Historical Records and Source Material*. Vol. I, Haifa, 1958.

Turkow, Jonas. *Azoy iz es Geven*. Buenos Aires, 1948.

Turkow, Jonas. *In Kamf farn Lebn*. Buenos Aires, 1949.

Wohl, Michael G., and Goodhart, Robert S. (eds.). *Modern Nutrition in Health and Disease*. Philadelphia, 1960.

The Black Book: The Nazi Crime against the Jewish People (no editor). New York, 1946.

Im Feuer Vergangen: Tagebücher aus dem Ghetto (no editor). Berlin, 1959.

PERIODICALS

American Journal of Clinical Nutrition, vol. iii, #6, 513.

Bleter far Geshichte. Publication of the Jewish Historical Institute in Warsaw.

  Babitz Benjamin, *"Notizen fun Ghetto, Lager, un Felder,"* vol. x (1957), 155.

  Bernshtein, T., "Vegn di Hitleristishe Metoden fun der Eksploitatsie fun Varshever Ghetto," vol. xii (1959), 58.

  Bieletzki, L., "Vegn der 'Aktsie' in Varshever Yidish Shpital dem 18 Januar 1943," vol. i (1948), 211.

  Document (German), "Economic Sector of Jewish Residential District of Warsaw, Order of April 19, 1941," vol xii (1959), 65.

  Ringelblum, Emanuel, "Fun di Letzten Notizen," vol. xi (1958), 20.

Helweg-Larsen, Per, *et al.* "Famine Disease in German Concentration Camps and Sequelae," *Acta Psychiatra et Neurologica Scandinavica.*

"Likwidacja Żydowskiej Warszawy," Biuletyn Żydowskiego Instytutu Historycznego, #1 (1951), 116.

Yad Washem Studies on the European Jewish Catastrophe and Resistance, vol. iv, Jerusalem, 1960.

YIVO Annual of Jewish Social Science, New York, Trunk, Isaiah: "Epidemics and Mortality in the Warsaw Ghetto," vol. viii, 1953, p. 94.

YIVO Bleter: publication of YIVO Institute of Jewish Research, Trunk, Isaiah: *"Melchomo kegn Yidn durch Farshpreitn Krankheit,"* vol. 37, 1953, p. 113.

NEWSPAPERS

Gazeta Żydowska, #125, December 17, 1941 (official German publication, printed in Polish, for Jews).

Głos Warszawy, #6, January 26, 1943 (organ of the Polish underground).

PERSONAL COMMUNICATIONS
(letters, questionnaires, interviews)

Doctors Witold Orłowski, Henri Fenigstein, Z. Askanas, T. Goliborska, Roman Kocen, Chaim Einhorn, Israel Rom, Leo Heller, T. Stabholz, Leon Wulman, Marek Wirecki, D. Krysiek, K. Zakrzewski.

Mr. and Mrs. Alfred Pozarik (accountant and nurse at the Czysta Hospital).

Mrs. Rose Odess (administrator), Mrs. K. Svedosh (nurse).

Mr. Isaac Zuckerman and Mr. Jonas Turkow (active leaders in Ghetto movements).

Index